POISON
Sorcery and Science · Friend and Foe

Sorcery and Science **POISON** *Friend and Foe*

Dieter Martinetz/Karlheinz Lohs

Edition Leipzig

Translated from the German by
Alistair and Alison Wightman

Martinetz, Dieter:
Poison: sorcery and science; friend
and foe / Dieter Martinetz; Karlheinz
Lohs. [Translated from the German by
Alistair u. Alison Wightman]. –
1. Aufl. – Leipzig: Edition Leipzig, 1987. –
165 S.: 145 Ill. EST: Gift ‹engl.›.

© 1987 by Edition Leipzig
Licence No.: 600/89/87
Design: Hans-Jörg Sittauer
Produced by Grafische Werke Zwickau
Order No.: 594 504 0

ISBN: 3-361-00137-4

Manufactured in the German Democratic Republic

Contents

What is poison, and how does it work?

(A short introduction to toxicology)

This book is about poison; it is therefore also about life, because life has never existed on earth without poison. One might say that poisons are the counterpoint of life. Man has always known and feared them. But he has also made use of them both for beneficient and for malevolent purposes, from the earliest times until the present day. The concept of poison has always been a very emotive one, even for the "enlightened" generation of the computer and space age, because it is associated in the mind with suffering, distress and death. The authors of this book have tried to establish how justifiable this view of poisons is, what poisons are, why some substances are considered poisonous, which poisons are of particular significance to man, as well as to the plant and animal worlds, and finally what man can do to prevent himself from being poisoned and to avoid contaminating his environment.

It goes without saying that a publication about poisons must begin by defining this term. For this, we must turn to the science of toxicology, the study of poisons.

But even this first concrete question about a definition of poison poses scientists specializing in toxicology with a dilemma, because there is no simple answer to the question as it stands, even though much has of course been written on the subject which is both intelligent and enlightening.

As so often in science, the reason for not being able to answer a question posed about nature is that the wrong question is being asked. Thus it is obviously wrong to ask, "What is poison?" Many centuries were to pass before the great late mediaeval naturalist and physician Theophrastus Bombastus von Hohenheim (better known as Paracelsus) realized that there was no absolute definition of poison, but that it was a question of quantity. Even in ancient times, however, it was known that certain plants could both kill and cure. This realization might be said to have ushered in the age when poison lore began to have a scientific basis. But another four hundred years were to elapse before it was understood that the question should really be "In what circumstances does a substance act as a poison?"

Toxicology has of course penetrated far deeper into the relationship between the quantity of a substance and its toxic properties since the days when Paracelsus realized that almost any substance can be poisonous if administered in the appropriate quantity. We know today that there are other significant factors which render a substance poisonous apart from the mere quantity it contains of substances with a harmful or even fatal effect on an organism. The most important of these factors is the way in which the toxic substance enters the organism.

It is common knowledge that the bite of some snakes can be fatal, because their venom quickly takes effect once it has entered the victim's bloodstream, unless an antiserum is injected at once. But it is also well known that the victim of a snakebite can be saved even by a layman, if the latter immediately sucks the venom from the wound; he suffers no ill effects even if he swallows the venom. Snake venom, which is made up of polymolecular protein, is quickly broken down by the gastro-intestinal tract like any other protein, without the least harmful effect.

The example of snake venom can also be used to demonstrate the varying sensitivity of different organisms to individual poisons. While the bites of various species of snake can be fatal to man and to many other animals, a hedgehog, for example, can be bitten by most poisonous snakes without its life being endangered. Moreover, the hedgehog is their natural enemy and an efficient snake-killer: after the Second World War, the Black Sea coast of Bulgaria and the Adriatic coast of Yugoslavia could only be developed as tourist areas after a large number of hedgehogs had been released to wipe out the snakes indigenous to these regions.

There are many other examples of varying sensitivity to poison: for instance, birds can safely eat deadly nightshade berries, which are extremely poisonous to humans, while on the other hand many species of bird can even serve as biochemical indicators. They warn of the presence of a number of toxic gases such as carbon monoxide, prussic acid or phosgene, reacting to them at levels where they are still totally harmless to other animals or to man. Physical or chemical properties, as well as biological characteristics, can be an important factor in the toxicity of a substance. The solubility of a substance in the body (whether in water, fat, lymph or blood) is an important criterion for determining toxicity; this is in general directly dependent on the nature of the chemical bond, which in turn is closely linked to the molecular structure of the substance.

For example, some substances are extremely toxic if drunk or injected into the body because of their high level of solubility in water, while they are completely harmless in water-insoluble compounds. To take one example from the many, the water-soluble salts of the element barium are extremely toxic, whilst barium sulphate, a water-insoluble barium salt, is used in a number of X-ray contrast media without any harmful effects. Because of its insolubility it leaves the body without undergoing any chemical change. Mercury provides another example of the link between solubility and toxicity. If, say, a small child bites through a thermometer and swallows the mercury it contains, it might indeed be at risk from the injuries caused by splinters of glass, but the mercury will have no harmful effect, because it is not dissolved in the gastro-intestinal tract and is therefore not toxic. If, however, the same metallic mercury is inhaled as vapour over a relatively long period (i.e. weeks, months or years), at a concentration greater than the limit which is considered safe, then serious symptoms of chronic poisoning are certain to ensue. Similarly, immediate, i.e. acute poisoning can

result if an aqueous solution of mercury(II)-chloride is drunk, whether accidentally or with the intention of committing murder or suicide.

The above suggests that time, too, plays a part in whether or not a substance will have toxic effects. We must examine this point in more detail. If one first considers the length of time during which an organism is exposed to a poison, certain gases demonstrate quite clearly that the effect over a short period of exposure to an extremely toxic gas is comparable with that of exposure to a less toxic gas over a longer period, i.e. the product of the concentration of the poison and the survival time is constant. In formula language this is written $c \times t = const.$, and is known as the ct product. It was first proved empirically by the chemist Fritz Haber in 1915. This formula is not applicable in all cases, but it can be useful as a sort of rule of thumb. At the very least, it witnesses clearly to the importance of the role played by time in cases of poisoning. We have already pointed out that the rapid passage of metallic mercury through the gastro-intestinal tract cannot result in poisoning. In this relatively short period, not enough mercury dissolves in the "organic juices" (e.g. gastric acid), so there is no absorption; mercury does not enter the bloodstream, and it is not transported to the bioactive centres vulnerable to this element. On the other hand, continuous inhalation of tiny quantities of mercury vapour—e.g. in the atmosphere at one's place of work—has a long-term effect, because these small doses can accumulate over weeks, months or even years, enabling the poison to build up a kind of stock in the body which it uses as the basis of its activity, or where it is easily accessible in sufficient concentration under certain metabolic conditions. The bone marrow or a specific organ such as the kidney may harbour such toxic deposits. Hairs can also store poison over a long period.

As some of these poisons are very stable, it is often possible, by locating such reserves, to find proof of poisoning even after the death of an organism. In the days when arsenic (arsenic trioxide) was a "fashionable" poison, this phenomenon was the undoing of many a poisoner.

Today, analytical methods of this type occasionally help to expose those responsible for pollution. Examples of such pollution include the illegal dumping of toxic heavy-metal compounds or of waste oil and surfactants by industrial cleaning plants, or of numerous agricultural chemicals (e.g. organochlorine compounds) in rivers, lakes and seas. Agricultural chemicals can be deposited in certain organs and in the body fat as extremely stable chemical after-products, so it is possible at a later date to prove that they have been used, often illegally. We can all call to mind cases where fish have been poisoned, where particularly endangered bird species have suffered great losses, and where residues of crop protection chemicals and pesticides or psychotropic agents have been found in the flesh of cattle.

The length of time one is exposed to a poison or has it stored within oneself is not, however, the only time factor involved in the effectiveness of a poison. Research in the last few decades has discovered that the toxicity of materials can be dependent on chronobiological factors, i.e. there is a relation between the point in time when the poison is administered and the intensity of the symptoms of poisoning. Depending on their characteristics, some poisons have a greater or lesser effect at midnight than in the morning or evening. There is even some evidence that the toxicity of certain poisons follows a monthly cycle. This is because of a number of metabolic processes, some of which we do not yet fully understand, such as enzyme and hormone levels, which fluctuate from individual to individual.

The peculiarities of metabolism are not only important as far as time is concerned, however; it would be more accurate to say that numerous metabolic processes play a direct or indirect role in poisoning. Some metabolic processes can render a poison totally harmless, but it is also possible for the organism concerned to react by converting foreign material into a harmful substance. Metabolic processes are not, however, as uniform as they might at first appear: there are differences between human races as well as within a particular race or even group of people, which can result in poisons being much more effective in some cases than in others. For example, it is known that coloured people are more sensitive to certain skin poisons than "whites", and because Europeans have different levels of a particular enzyme, they react differently to synthetic inhibitors of this enzyme. Such inhibitors are extremely practical as medicaments and as pesticides, so this is of decisive toxicological importance. Even the metabolism of an individual is far from constant, so the effects of poisoning are not absolutely predictable; the health of the individual plays a role, as do the type and quantity of the food he consumes and the stimulants he takes. Even "mental health" has a biochemical effect on the metabolism—stress, anxiety, depression, etc.—and has a direct influence upon the seriousness of poisoning.

It is a curious fact—though not without practical importance—that man, animals and plants can, within certain limits, become accustomed to poison. In other words, certain metabolic processes can adjust to the introduction of poisonous matter, and so the organism concerned can tolerate a higher level of poison than other organisms. It is common knowledge that smokers develop nicotine habituation (which does not, of course, protect them from the long-term harmful effects of smoking). The same is true of drug addicts; they actually become addicted to poison. This can also occur when certain medicinal drugs are prescribed over a long period. Sometimes extreme cases of poison habituation occur in nature. For example, it has long been known that in certain Alpine regions (e.g. Styria), the inhabitants use highly-toxic arsenic as a stimulant, and over the years they acquire a tolerance of quantities which would kill anyone else instantly.

The customs and police forces of certain countries make use of the metabolic poison habituation of animals for finding drugs, among other things. Dogs are regularly given small quantities of a drug and thus become addicted, so that finally their craving for the substance makes them react extremely sensitively to certain narcotics—hashish, cocaine, etc. The poison habituation of plants, limited as it is, has a widespread practical function in that tree, shrub and grass species which have developed this habituation can be grown in areas of high pollution. Otherwise, areas with a high concentration of power stations and chemical and metallurgical plants would look barren indeed!

Closer research into the biochemical reasons for such toleration and for poison habituation is still in its initial stages. But we should not place our hopes too high as far as the invulnerability of our biosphere and its inhabitants to poison is concerned. The problem of acid rain and of dying woods has made this particularly clear. If the reader re-considers the circumstances in which a substance acts as a poison, he is bound to come to the conclusion that "poison" is an extremely complex phenomenon and cannot be encompassed by a short definition.

Even though there has been—and is—no shortage of attempts to establish rules or even to postulate laws by comparing the chemical structure of a poisonous compound—or merely of a biologically active substance—and its potential toxic effect, it is sufficiently clear from the influence of the factors described above and others which have not been named that chemistry and toxicology cannot furnish such rules or laws. Chemical structure/toxic effect relationships do, however, exist within strict limitations in selected chemical classes or groups of substances, but unfortunately one cannot generalize about them.

The following examples of such relationships in poisons are given to show firstly how useful theories which start out as pure hypotheses can be, and secondly to draw attention to the limits beyond which scientists have not yet been able to advance in their attempts to discover mechanisms of action. The reader will understand without detailed explanation that it is beyond the scope of this book to give a detailed account of such a fundamental and disparate complex of problems.

The physician and researcher Paul Ehrlich, whose investigations of organic arsenic compounds won world renown, attempted to find a link between their effects and their molecular structures. The basis of his speculations and of the experimental studies which backed them up was the success (and lack of success) which colour chemists had achieved in the preceding decades in explaining the relationships between the chemical structure and the colour or colouring properties of a molecule. Ehrlich's discovery of salvarsan brought about our victory over a great scourge of mankind, syphilis. It bore impressive witness to his working hypothesis which was based on chemical structure/effect relationships, a hypothesis which stimulated many research projects, particularly in the pharmaceutical industry, in the decades which followed. Proof of the success of such projects in this industry were the impressive results achieved by Gerhard Domagk and others in the field of sulphonamide chemotherapeutants, e.g. the sulphachrysoidine and thiacetazone group, the development of antibiotics and research into some groups of psychotropic agents, such as benzodiazepines and piperidyl benzilates. Pesticides are the foremost of the poisons most widely discussed by the general public today. Here, too, theoretical concepts and experiments derived from these have led to the identification of chemical structure/effect relationships in selected classes, although much that seemed promising in this area has not borne fruit.

Highly active organophosphorous esters provide a particularly illustrative example in the history of toxicology in general and of toxicological research in the field of pesticides in particular of the usefulness of a fruitful working hypothesis in identifying a new class. This family has been widely known since the 19th century; Karl Arnold Michaelis in Germany and Alexandr Arminingeldovich Arbusov in Tsarist Russia were particularly important pioneers in this area, which had previously been considered as purely academic, at the turn of the century. But it was a young chemist called Gerhard Schrader from the Bayer plants in Leverkusen and Wuppertal-Elberfeld, which were then part of the IG-Farben empire, who discovered the great practical importance of synthetic organophosphorous compounds in the work which he began in 1935; he thus gave an important stimulus, which is still felt today, to chemistry, toxicology, hygienics and, unfortunately, the development of chemical weapons.

During the early period of his studies, after evaluating the initial findings of the products of his syntheses, which he had verified by experimentation on animals, Schrader drew up a basic formula. Grossly simplified,

$$Y-P \overset{\displaystyle O[S]}{\underset{\displaystyle X_2}{\big<}}X_1$$

this formula states that biologically active organophosphorous compounds will always occur when the element phosphorus as a pentavalent central atom is combined with oxygen or sulphur and two alkyl or alkoxyl groupings (X_1 or X_2) and an organic or inorganic acid group (Y).

The most dangerous military poisons known today, namely organophosphorous chemical weapons of the tabun, sarin, soman and VX groups, as well as a large number of extremely useful pesticides, were developed using this formula.

The experience gained in decades of toxicological research has taught us that to judge the effect of a poison on an organism—whether human, animal or vegetable—it is of the first importance to ascertain the nature of the chemical reaction. This reactivity depends not only on the molecular structure of the poison, but also very much on the "molecular environment", i.e. biological conditions in the affected organs and tissues. This brings us back to what we said initially about the conditions in which poisoning occurs, and at this point we must conclude this short introduction to toxicology. We have not been able to do more than scratch the surface of a large and complex scientific discipline which has numerous interconnections with chemistry and medicine and with other natural and social sciences.

Even today, toxicology is still not regarded as an independent field of study. As a science, it is one of those special fields which have emerged only in the last hundred years because of their ever increasing independence. In the first half of this century, toxicology was still treated by universities and colleges as a branch of pharmacology. Even today, certain teaching and training centres are known as institutes of "pharmacology and toxicology" and are part of a medical faculty. In earlier centuries, toxicology was often linked to pharmacy in the narrower sense of the word. That is why dispensing chemists are traditionally believed, even nowadays, to be particularly knowledgeable about natural and synthetic poisons which can be used in suitably small doses for therapeutic purposes.

These facts must be taken into account if the structure of this book is to be understood. The sequence of the individual chapters is not dictated by any generally accepted rule, just as there is no obligatory order for the treatment of individual facts in textbooks or lectures or in training programmes. Although we begin with poison in the plant world and end with industrially produced synthetic toxins, this sequence is entirely arbitrary. However, this order is of practical value to the reader, and will therefore be found to be the same or similar to that used in some other books about poisons. It was not our intention to write a textbook, but rather to explain and to stimulate the reader to develop his interest in the subject. We have also tried to show just how powerful poison can be, and to tell the reader about historical events or social problems, and sometimes merely to relate anecdotes from the past.

It is inevitable that the reader will occasionally have to cross-refer to facts, events and relationships, because the problems discussed are often very complex. The following chapters begin by discussing poisonous drugs and intoxicating extracts, mostly of vegetable origin. Here we encounter potent toxins and the more harmless stimulants found in coffee, tea or cola, which are innocuous in normal use.

After looking at stimulants, narcotics and fungi, we will examine members of the plant world which we are familiar with on account of their beautiful colours, shapes and scents, but whose toxic potential is usually known only to the toxicologist or the natural product chemist, or to the pharmacologist who can take advantage of it.

The fifth chapter deals with animal poisons, which in terms of both their structure and their effect exhibit considerable variations from poisons in the plant world, and just as many similarities and parallels. In the realm of poisonous animals too, it quickly becomes clear that enquiring man has not penetrated nearly far enough into the complex workings of nature: even if a work of several volumes can be written about these special animal poisons, scientists still have generations of work ahead of them before they will be able fully to understand this aspect of toxicology.

The reader might consider mineral poisons at first sight to be out of place in a study of toxicology, but they include some of the oldest known biologically active compounds. One only has to think of arsenic, which came to be regarded as the quintessence of poison, and which has been responsible for many murders and suicides over the centuries.

The final chapter deals with synthetic poisons, because man has imitated nature in the field of toxicology too, and in some cases has even surpassed her. It goes without saying that a comprehensive description of synthetic poisons alone would fill several volumes, because these now number thousands. Within the framework of this book, this section is intended merely to round off our excursion through the world of poisons.

The book will have fulfilled its purpose if it is laid aside with the feeling that one has learnt something, but enjoyed the experience. The bibliography will enable the reader to elicit further information.

Stimulation, intoxication and death

(Poisonous drugs and intoxicating extracts)

Narcotics. Substances which influence the psyche and therefore human behaviour in one way or another are known collectively as psychotropic. There are several groups of these, two important ones being euphoriants and hallucinogens. The former comprise substances which create a feeling of happiness with no objective foundation. Hallucinogens, on the other hand, evoke optical and acoustic hallucinations which have no basis in reality. Psychotropic substances can be assigned to one or other of these groups depending on the mental state they induce. They are commonly described indiscriminately as drugs or narcotics.

Apart from a few exceptions, natural psychotropics occur exclusively in the plant world. In the quantities used for intoxication, most of these create a temporary and reversible change in the state of consciousness. The actual toxic effect results from taking an overdose or from using the drug over a period of months, years or even decades.

Among the drugs of classical Antiquity and the Middle Ages which were shrouded in mystery were various species of the nightshade family (Solanaceae). Although these have a marked intoxicating effect, they also have extremely toxic side-effects, and for this reason are no longer widely used today. Apart from the mandrake *(Mandragora officinarum)*, which flourishes in southern Europe, the deadly nightshade *(Atropa belladonna)*, black henbane *(Hyoscyamus niger)* and thornapple *(Datura stramonium)* were particularly important in Central Europe. The generic name *Atropa* is derived from Greek. Atropos was the third of the three Fates, in whose hands lay the predetermined fate, life and death of mankind.

The active principles of deadly nightshade and henbane are (S)-hyoscyamine and smaller amounts of atropine and scopolamine, which are all tropane alkaloids. It was not until the 20th century that the chemical structure of these very complex natural substances

was ascertained in any detail. The German Nobel Prize laureate Richard Willstädter was closely involved with this work. (S)-hyoscyamine is also one of the main alkaloids present in the thornapple which, according to tradition, was brought from Asia by gypsies in the 16th century. Of biochemical interest is the fact that as the fruit ripens the (S)-hyoscyamine is converted into atropine.

The tropane alkaloids become active when parts of the plant are chewed, an infusion of these is drunk, or when an ointment made from the whole plant or parts of it is rubbed into the skin. The atropine then acts as a powerful stimulant to the central nervous system, whilst scopolamine, which is closely related to it in chemical terms, has the opposite effect. As different combinations of alkaloids occur in different plants and plant parts, the affected person will, depending on the drugs taken, either show signs of great stimulation (singing, dancing and conversing with people who are not present), or he will sink into a trance and react like someone under hypnosis, with greatly diminished willpower, great suggestibility, but fluent and coherent speech. This phase is sometimes succeeded by a deep sleep accompanied by vivid dreams which appear real—the victim often imagines he has been changed into an animal (e.g. the belief in werewolves), has erotic dreams or imagines he is flying.

Some tropane alkaloids are currently used for medicinal purposes, such as to alleviate convulsions in the gastro-intestinal area, and to inhibit the secretion of mucous in the respiratory tract as a preparation for anaesthesia. Because of its specific inhibiting effect on vomiting, scopolamine is used as a remedy for sea sickness.

In everyday life, children are particularly at risk from these poisons, because they are easily tempted to taste the bright berries of the deadly nightshade or the fruit of the thornapple. As little as 1 g of thornapple seeds is a

ıatal dose for small children, and two or three deadly nightshade berries can kill a child if immediate medical assistance is not sought.

It is scarcely surprising that such powerful plant constituents have always excited interest.

The Abbess Hildegard of Bingen wrote that depression and love-sickness could be eased by the mandrake. The scholastic philosopher Count Albert of Bollstädt, better known as Albertus Magnus, knew the intoxicating and narcotic effect of mandrake plants, and in the 13th century Roger of Salerno referred in his *Practica Chirurgiae* to the smoke of henbane as an early form of anaesthesia for toothache. Such early scientific observations aside, however, wild speculation and rumour about the effects of plant constituents fed superstition for centuries.

Tropane alkaloids belong to the large group of hallucinogens which attack the biochemistry of man's central nervous system in a way we still do not fully understand, causing serious sensory derangement and a disturbed mental state. The particular characteristic of this group is that almost all of the phenomena experienced during intoxication appear real (in contrast to hallucinogenic derivatives of lysergic acid, tryptamine and phenylethylamine, where the "trip" is usually experienced from the viewpoint of a detached onlooker; we will return to this later).

Let us first examine the effects of "flying mixtures", which science has still not divested of mystery. In 1954 Siegbert Ferckel gave a very graphic description of an experiment he had carried out on himself, not without personal risk, using such a "flying mixture". Although its exact composition is unknown today, deadly nightshade, henbane and thornapple were undoubtedly the main ingredients. After rubbing the ointment all over his chest, particularly around the heart, Ferckel rapidly felt its effects. He described them as follows: "Less than five minutes had elapsed before my heart began to beat wildly and I was overcome by a powerful sensation of dizziness ... my face was totally distorted; my pupils were almost as large as the eyeballs themselves, my lips were bluish and very swollen, and my whole face was chalky-white ... Suddenly the walls and ceiling began

Belief in werewolves was widespread in the Middle Ages. Hallucinations resulting from the taking of drugs from the nightshade family are known, time
and again, to take the form of imagined animal metamorphosis.

to undulate and to crash together with a loud bang ... Faces came towards me out of the darkness ... It slowly grew completely dark around me, and I soared upwards at great speed. It grew light again, and I saw hazily, through a pink veil, that I was floating above the town. The figures which had oppressed me before in my room accompanied me on this flight through the clouds ..."

The main features of Ferckel's description tally with those to be found in the interrogation protocols of witch trials in the 13th to 18th centuries. But ointments of this type must have been known even in classical Antiquity, judging from the writings of poets and philosophers of that period. For example, Lucian writes the following of

a sorceress in his *Onos* (Ass): "... Hereupon she opened a fairly large chest containing a large quantity of boxes, and took one of them out; what was actually inside it I cannot say, except that it looked to me like oil. She then rubbed it in all over her body, from her toenails to her hair, and suddenly feathers burst out all over her, her nose became a crooked beak, she took on all the characteristics of a bird which distinguish it from other animals, and in short stopped being what she was and turned into a raven ..." Here again we find the phenomenon of animal metamorphosis which we mentioned before.

The opinion is expressed in some of the pharmacological and toxicological literature that these hallucinations were caused by wolfsbane *(Aconitum napellus)*, which was added to some of these "flying mixtures", and thus by the alkaloid aconitine which it contains. This aconitine first stimulates the sensitive nerve endings in the skin, then paralyzes them. Thus, particularly when one is intoxicated, it is quite possible to feel that one is growing feathers or fur.

From the vantage point of today, we can see that the "flying mixtures" of the Middle Ages were intoxicants and stimulants for the poorest sections of the community, who tried to escape their miserable lot by hallucinations—which appeared real to them—of flight, metamorphosis, lavish feasts, dancing and eroticism. A present-day analogy can be found in the use of drugs by drop-outs, whether in Brooklyn, Amsterdam or Stockholm, among West Berlin's child prostitutes or in the shanty towns of Latin America, Asia and Africa. In the last twenty or thirty years, new information has reached us from outside Europe about the use of different species of the nightshade family as intoxicants. Australian Aborigines, for example, smoke the leaves of a species of *Duboisia*, African tribes smoke the leaves of a species of thornapple *(Datura fastuosa)*, and the natives of Peru and Colombia brew a drink called tonga from the

Preceding page:
For a long time, it was the apothecaries which were entitled to deal in poisons and cures, but university courses for them were not introduced in Prussia until 1825.
View of an 18th century apothecary's laboratory from Berka (Thuringia).
Thüringer Museum, Eisenach.

From time immemorial, man has known how to use plant constituents for both beneficent and malevolent purposes. One medicinal plant which we can no longer identify was known to the Greeks as *silphium*, presumably an *Asant* species no longer in existence. The plant was obviously very important—the king himself supervised the weighing and packing of it. Painting of Arcesilaos from the Vulci School, *c.* 565–560 B.C.
Cabinet des Médailles, Paris.

A physician—probably Andromachus—supervising the gathering of medicinal plants.
Book illumination from Kitab ad-diryaq, 1199. Ms. arabe 2964, f.22.
Bibliothèque Nationale, Paris.

From the 15th to the 17th century, sorcery and witchcraft cults were widespread in Europe. Magic lotions and love potions were widely available and found a ready market.
Frans Francken the Younger, *Witches' coven* (detail), 1607.
Kunsthistorisches Museum, Vienna.

Paracelsus, a physician and naturalist, was a pioneer in providing a scientific
foundation for toxicology.
Painting from the Rubens School, Brussels.

In apothecaries exquisitely crafted pieces were often used to store medicaments and poisons: Rococo poison cabinet from the former Jesuit chemist's shop in Györ, supported by a Moor, which was practically symbolic of chemist's shops in some countries.
Széchenyi apothecary, Györ (Hungary).

The mandrake *(Mandragora officinarum)*, whose root was used in the preparation of liquors and ointments and worn as an amulet, is presented to the physician Dioscorides by an allegorical figure.
Miniature from Codex med. Graec., 1, f.4., *c.* 520.
Österreichische Nationalbibliothek, Vienna.

The belief in the efficacy of aphrodisiacs was expressed in classical literature and painting. *Love spell*. Painting by a Master from the Lower Rhine, *c.* 1480. Museum der bildenden Künste, Leipzig.

The "flying mixtures" of centuries past, in which species of the nightshade family were the main ingredient, were simply narcotics and stimulants for the poorest sections of the population. They produced a wide range of hallucinatory experiences. In the illustration, these take the form of erotic visions, belief in one's ability to fly, animal metamorphosis and drinking bouts.

Michael Herz, *Witches' Sabbath on Walpurgis Night on the Blocksberg Mountain* (detail). Copperplate engraving, 17th century.

orange-red thornapple *Brugmansia sanguinea*. Other species of *Datura* and *Hyoscyamus* are also used in one way or another as intoxicants today.

In 1770, in his account of a journey through Russia, Samuel Gottlieb Gmelin related that Cossacks added thornapple seeds to their beer to make it more potent. This method of "spiking" beer was already known in ancient China and among other Asiatic peoples. The practice seems to have been widespread in Europe, too, from the Middle Ages on.

Police regulations in the German town Eichstätt, in Central Franconia, stipulated in 1507 that brewers must not add henbane seeds to beer, under penalty of a fine of five Gulden. Practices of this sort must have resulted in poisoning in quite a few cases, because the quantities required for intoxication are also sufficient to produce a variety of toxic effects, from dryness of the mouth to palpitations and impairment of vision over a long period. Consumption of large amounts can result in death from respiratory paralysis.

As early as the 14th century, Konrad von Megenberg wrote in his book *De naturis rerum*: "One should not give the seed to anyone to eat, because it kills and brings the languishing illness of oblivion, so that one only wishes to sleep and forgets many things." In his *Kraeuterbuch* (Herbal), which was published in Basle in 1664, Jacobus Theodorus Tabernaemontanus warns, "No-one should drink beer with henbane seeds except those who have forfeited their lives, because doing so results in frenzy of the brain, loss of reason and sometimes sudden death."

In the Middle Ages drugs of this type were sometimes mixed into the food of others as a practical joke, so that one could laugh at their intoxication. In his *Magiae naturalis*, which appeared in Naples in 1581, Giambattista della Porta explained how one could make people go mad for a day at banquets for one's own amusement, without impairing their health. He named the mandrake, deadly nightshade and thornapple as means to this end.

Many similar applications could be quoted from the literature. But let us now turn to another peculiarity of narcotic nightshade drugs, because they are among the oldest ingredients used in the preparation of so-called love potions (aphrodisiacs). In the East, the mandrake was most commonly used for this purpose. Its Hebrew name, "dûdaim", suggests this, because "dûd" means "to love". Many people in that region today still believe in the effectiveness of such stimulants. Agents of this type have also found their way into classical literature—for example, in Act 1 Scene 3 of *Othello*, Shakespeare writes that Desdemona's father, on learning of Othello's marriage to his daughter, accuses him of bewitching her with love potions.

The ingredients of love potions are poisons which either attack the central nervous system—this has already been mentioned in connection with the deadly nightshade—or stimulate the genitals by vasodilatation, as is the case with preparations of Spanish fly *(Lytta vesicatoria)*, to which we shall return later. In 1697 scholars at Leipzig University declared that love could be compelled by love potions and other "magic devices". But even in Antiquity, some scholars and poets doubted that such effects could be achieved. Ovid, for instance, in his *Ars amandi*, declares that "Deceived is he whoever has recourse to Haemonian arts ... Medean herbs will not keep love alive, nor Marsian charm united to magic sounds."

Justinian I equated love potions with sorcery, and condemned offenders of the lower classes to be crucified or thrown to wild animals in accordance with the *Lex Cornelia*; members of the upper classes were executed by hanging or poisoning.

In 18th-century Prussia, common law still prescribed penalties for peddling love potions. Should their usage result in death, the supplier faced a sentence of ten to fifteen years' fortress imprisonment.

If one reads the advertisements in the international press nowadays, one might believe one had been transported back to the Middle Ages or to Antiquity, because aphrodisiacs of this kind seem to attract just as many byers now as then. Even so-called "modern man" is still fascinated by magic lotions and love potions—whether out of genuine scientific interest or in a commercially encouraged search for emotional fulfilment, be it forgetfulness, pleasure, escapism or vicarious fantasies.

Lotions made from nightshades are apparently used for more than just sexual pleasure; even today, they are used by many tribes to achieve religious ecstasy. Some peoples have shown a preference for infusions made

Some Central and South American Indian tribes used "yákee" as a stimulant. It is a powder obtained from the seeds of various trees and contains tryptamine derivatives. Flowering branch of *Virola calophylloidea*, and a native taking snuff. Drawing by E. W. Smith from: *Botanic Museum*, Leafits Haward University, Vol. 16 (1954), 4.

from nightshades, such as the tonga drink prepared by the medicine men of the Peruvian Indians. After the intoxication had subsided, the visions experienced were related to an awed "audience" as conversations with the gods or with the spirits of their ancestors.

Drugs of this type were also used by various oracles of Greek Antiquity, especially those dedicated to the god Apollo, after whom the Greek term for henbane, *Apollinaris*, is named. The German toxicologist Hermann Georg Fühner studied in detail accounts of how the Pythia (priestess of Apollo) in Delphi became "clairvoyant". In his publications on the subject, he describes her ecstasy as being identical to that of the Peruvian Indians after drinking tonga.

Let us now turn to some other interesting hallucinogens. Mexican drugs, for instance, are still shrouded in mystery. One old magic drug made from the seeds of the morning glory *Rivea corymbosa*, which the Aztecs referred to as "ololiuqui", is still used for magic rites by Zapotec Indians on occasion. The seeds of another species of morning glory, *Ipomoea violacea*, are still used in similar way. Apart from other lysergic acid derivatives, the main active principle in these drugs is d-lysergic acid amide (ergine).

Francisco Hernández de Toledo, who was the royal physician at the Spanish Court, described the effect of ololiuqui as follows: "In powdered form or as a decoction … it acts as an aphrodisiac … In earlier times, when the priests wished to speak with their gods and to receive messages from them, they ate this plant, so as to enter a state of delirium. Thousands of visions and satanic hallucinations appeared to them."

The poisonous ergot fungus *(Claviceps purpurea)* also contains this type of lysergic acid derivative. It is true that we are jumping the gun a little here, because we will be looking at poisonous fungi later, but this is justified here, since we are after all discussing hallucinogens. In 1943 the Swiss chemist Albert Hofmann

synthesized a derivative of this acid, diethylamide, with the laboratory name LSD_{25}. It was purely by chance that Hofmann noticed the extreme effects of the new chemical compound he had produced. Even tiny amounts of 20 to 50 µg of LSD result in serious mental disturbance such as hallucinations, visions in colour and other conditions symptomatic of intoxication. Today, LSD is considered the most powerful of all artificial stimulants; it can also cause genetic damage. However, some scientists see LSD "only" as an introductory drug which paves the way to the addictive use of hard drugs, such as heroin, cocaine, etc. It is particu-

» 27 «

larly easy for the addict to take an overdose of drugs whose dose is measured in microgrammes: instead of a "journey to paradise", he or she experiences hell ("bad trips"), and death can ensue. But it is not only an overdose which can be fatal. The addict also greatly over-estimates his own abilities during intoxication. It is widely known that people under the influence of LSD have stood in the path of cars and trains in the delusion that they can stop them. Others, firmly convinced that they can fly, leap out of windows.

LSD has other "Mexican relations". In Central America there is an ancient Teonanácatl cult, of which the object is a "sacred mushroom" *(Psilocybe mexicana)*, which produces an ancient Aztec narcotic. It is worshipped in the form of stone sculptures of mushrooms, which are more than three thousand years old. Extracts of fungi, mixed with milk or pulque, are consumed mainly during cult rites. The Spaniards who conquered the Aztec empire under Hernán Cortés, full of missionary zeal, denounced these practices as the work of the Devil. The main active substances are the tryptamine derivatives psilocybin and psilocin. Their structure is closely related to that of the bufotenine in toad poison and the neurotransmitter serotonin.

Various Indian tribes in Central and South America have used snuff called "cohoba" (yopo) and "yákee" (daricá, epéna and yakwana), which contains other tryptamine derivatives. The natives use two small pipes to blow this powder into each other's nostrils. The seeds of trees of the genus *Anadenanthera* (Fabaceae), and seeds of species of *Virola* (Myristicaceae) are two sources of this drug.

The Mexican "treasure trove" also contains another very well-known hallucinogenic drug—peyote or peyotl, which is extracted from the succulent, spiny cactus of the same name. For a time, it bore the scientific name *Anhalonium Lewinii* in honour of the famous toxicologist Louis Lewin, but today it is known as *Lophophora william-*

sii. The central section of the cactus is cut and dried. The main active principle which it contains (up to four or seven percent), alongside numerous other phenolic and non-phenolic bases, is mescaline. In comparison with LSD, high doses of about 400mg of the pure substance are needed for intoxication. Mescaline was isolated by the Berlin pharmacologist Arthur Heffter in 1896.

Its effects were publicized in Kurt Beringer's monograph *Der Meskalinrausch* (The mescaline intoxication) of 1927: "Suddenly a drop of my right eyelid melts off and falls into the socket where the eyeball should be. My whole eyelid melts like wax; finally the root of my nose also caves in, and I can see a brightly lit slit stretching from the corner of one eye to the corner of the other, which makes me think of the opening in a money-box. A new figure appears, a head half-human and half-dog, with a long nose, which has a bright red tip, and bright red lips. A red drop falls from the tip of the nose, then more red drips and the nose melts inside: the skin from the bridge of the nose hangs down, and suddenly swings up, shining with grease, over the right eye and onto the forehead …"

The intoxicating ingredients of the nutmeg *(Myristica fragrans)* are, to a certain extent, structurally similar to mescaline. As long ago as 700 B.C., it was used in India and Arabia not only as a spice, but also as a medicine and as a means of heightening sexual urges. In the late 19th and early 20th centuries, nutmeg infusions were often used as abortifacients too, a fact which resulted in numerous cases of poisoning. Nutmeg was used as a narcotic after the Second World War, especially in the USA. Its effects became widely known mainly as a result of the autobiography of Malcolm X, the black leader of the Black Muslim sect, who was murdered during racial unrest in 1965. Even convicts have on occasion used the spice, which is easily available in prison kitchens, as a substitute for hashish. Its hallucinogenic effect is ascribed to myristicin and elemecin, both of

The nutmeg *(Myristica fragrans)* was known even in ancient India as an aphrodisiac and for its healing properties. In more recent times it has often been used as an abortifacient and a stimulant.

which are phenylallyl substances. The formation of amphetamines, which resemble mescaline, by transamination processes in the human body is discussed in the specialist toxicological literature. Myristicin has considerable toxic side-effects. The main symptoms of poisoning are headaches, dryness of the mouth and a general feeling of malaise.

Hashish—or marijuana—is one of the best-known narcotics today. It is extracted mainly from Indian hemp (*Cannabis sativa* var. *indica*). According to the Greek historian Herodotus, hashish was a very popular narcotic among the Scythians as long ago as 500 B.C.

They scattered the hemp seeds or small pieces of resin onto hot stones in an enclosed room and inhaled the smoke.

The hashishin (hemp eater) sect, from which the word "assassin" is derived, was scattered throughout Palestine and Syria, and won notoriety in the 11th century; one of the objectives of members of the sect was to assassinate their religious and political opponents. Their use of hashish may well have helped to turn them into willing murderers.

In the field of belles-lettres, the intoxication, hallucinations and visions induced by hemp have undoubtedly provided inspiration for writers on many occasions. Flying steeds and carpets, the wondrous appearance of magnificent palaces, caravans of camels laden with gold, and beautiful, amorous maidens are all typical of the famous *Arabian Nights*. The use of hashish is also mentioned in Boccaccio's *Decameron*. But most famous of all is Charles Baudelaire's vivid description of hashish intoxication which he, as a highly dependent addict, knew very well from personal experience, in his book *Les Paradis artificiels*, which was published in 1860 (the French poet was a member of "Le Club des Hashichins" in Paris).

Hemp still plays an important role in Islamic countries as a substitute for alcohol, whose use is prohibited by the Koran.

Today, hemp is the most widespread psychotropic plant in the world, and experts from the UN Commission of Narcotics estimate that its use has become habitual for between two and three hundred million people. The amount of the active substances it contains depends very much on climatic conditions. The "Green Turkish" and "Red Lebanese" varieties are considered mild, whilst the "Black Afghan" and the "Dark-brown Pakistani" are strong; the countries included in these names are some of the main producers, along with Mexico, Colombia and Nepal.

The names hashish and marijuana (the latter probably comes from the Spanish Christian names Maria and Juana) both refer to the same drug. Hashish is the resin which is pressed into chunks, while the dried and crushed leaves, which usually come from the female plant are known as marijuana. It is very easy to extract the resin; one method involves the peasants walking through the fields of flowering hemp wearing leather aprons. The resin adheres to the leather, and can later be scratched off with knives. The harvest is much greater if the entire flowering part of the plant is cut off and rubbed onto a carpet after drying. The resin gathers in the loops, and can then be beaten out. Its characteristic compounds are the cannabinols, and the intoxicating effect comes from the Δ^9-tetrahydrocannabinol. More than thirty specific constituents of hemp are known.

When one is under the influence of hashish, one remains fully conscious; relaxation and slight euphoria are accompanied by mainly optical hallucinations. Visions in brilliant colours have been described; sound perception is heightened, space seems to stretch away to eternity and all sense of time is lost. If taken orally, it is absorbed very slowly, and takes effect only after thirty to sixty minutes. People under the influence of hashish can quite easily develop a "split personality", causing them to lose all self-control and become violent for no apparent reason. Compared to opium, hashish has a relatively mild toxic effect. The fatal dose of its active principle is about 800 to 1400 mg of cannabinol per kg body weight, depending on the species affected. This is equivalent to 30 to 60 g of hashish. However, its chronic toxic effects should not be underestimated. Many hashish smokers complain of continual headaches, loss of memory and long-term difficulties in thinking clearly. These are obvious symptoms of a deterioration of the brain functions, and can be attributed to organic damage to the brain. Other chronic attendant symptoms are conjunctivitis, asthma and bronchitis.

Cocaine is a popular hard drug. It is a product of the coca shrub *(Erythroxylon coca)*, a plant which has long been cultivated in South America and in the Indonesian islands.

The traffic in hashish and marijuana plays a central role in the drugs scene in many western industrial states today. It is organized by gangs, and the percentage of undetected crime leads us to suspect that multi-million pound profits can be made by gangsters from drugs every year. The real crime of this trade is that users, mainly young people, are won over, and from using hashish graduate to hard drugs such as cocaine and heroin. This fact will be discussed in detail in the following. Let us now return to the euphoriants mentioned at the beginning. These are usually powerful habit-forming drugs. They are not characterized by hallucinations, like the drugs we have just been discussing, but,

in the initial stages, by a feeling of physical and mental well-being and of increased powers, then by a state of semi-consciousness which—e.g. in the case of opium smoking—is often accompanied by erotic dreams.

One of the ancient cultivated plants of South America and the Indonesian islands is the coca shrub *(Erythroxylon coca)*. Depending on its place of origin, the leaves contain various amounts of different alkaloids. The most important psychoactive alkaloid is cocaine, a tropane alkaloid. The main producer today is Peru.

Cocaine, which was isolated by Friedrich Wöhler and Albert Niemann in 1860, was the first highly-efficient local anaesthetic; today it is used in only a few cases in ear, nose and throat and eye surgery.

The cult of coca chewing was at first the preserve of Inca priests to whom the coca leaf was a symbol of divine power, but after the collapse of the mighty empire, it spread very rapidly through the countries of the Andes. Nowadays some 100,000 kg of the dried leaves are chewed in this area every year. The risk of addiction is very high, and it is usually even more difficult to kick the habit than is the case with morphine.

Cocaine, which is termed a hard drug, is usually sniffed. Overdoses can result in respiratory paralysis, but the drug has also been known to affect the cardiac muscle and kill in this way. The fatal dose for man is generally 1 g taken orally, and continual use can result in mental disorders.

The psychoanalyst Siegmund Freud was for a time a fanatical proponent of the use of cocaine in medicine; indeed, he took it himself to increase the strength of his muscles. His views were strongly opposed by the toxicologist Louis Lewin.

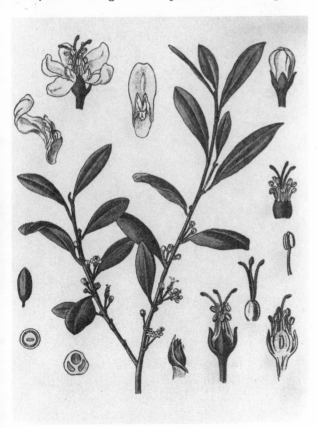

a series of 6-substituted 4-methoxy-pyrones (kawalactones), such as kawain. The actual effect of the drug has not yet been adequately explained.

The names of morphine, opium and the opium poppy *(Papaver somniferum)* are probably connected in everyone's mind with both poison and medication.

In his *Metamorphoses*, the Roman poet Ovid described Morpheus, the son of Somnus, the god of sleep, who has the power to conjure up dream figures. The ancient Greeks chose the poppy head as a symbol for their god Morpheus. The method of opium extraction by making an incision in the green capsule was well known to them. The opium poppy is thought to have been culti-

Let us turn now to another drug, the root of kava pepper *(Piper methysticum)*, which is known among the Pacific South Seas islanders as kava-kava, and has been cultivated since time immemorial. To prepare the drug, the peeled and cut roots are ritually chewed, then collected in a bowl and diluted with water. Chewing serves a purpose in that the spittle causes enzymatic decomposition to occur; water alone has little effect. Taking large amounts of this drug results in pronounced euphoria without hallucinations. Repeated use brings about addiction and physical harm. The root contains

vated on a large scale in Central Europe, the Middle East and Asia more than four thousand years ago. The use of this plant to alleviate pain is also known to us from writings dating back to about 700 B.C. Opium reached Roman doctors from Greece, and Andromachus, Nero's personal physician, included it in a medicine which was supposed to alleviate all ills. Such cure-alls are called alexipharmics, and have played an important part in medicine and alchemy for thousands of years. They were thought to protect against, or cure, individual, or indeed all cases of poisoning. Thus the theriac was thought to be a universal antidote, or *antidotum mithridadicum*; it contained opium and up to one hundred other ingredients, and people swore by it for centuries. The recipe is traditionally supposed to have been devised by King Mithridates of Pontus.

Opium was an important component of many such miracle cures. It is no exaggeration to say that, along with the alkaloids extracted from it, opium has never

been surpassed by any other plant constituent in terms of pharmaceutical, pharmacological and toxicological importance. Its name is even linked with wars. In the so-called Opium Wars (1840–1842 and 1856–1860) waged by Great Britain and France against China, an attempt was made to open up the Chinese market by the forced importation of opium into the country. The First Opium War, which was waged by Britain alone, broke out when the Imperial Commissioner Lin Tse-hsü destroyed twenty thousand cases of smuggled British opium on the orders of the court: the British reacted by imposing a blockade on Hong Kong.

Extensive areas of opium poppies continue to be cultivated today in the Middle and Far East. The drug is extracted by incising the green poppy capsules and col-

Needle for taking opium, and tongs for the coals to light the pipe. Persian chibouque stopped with plaster and with a hole in the side for smoking opium.

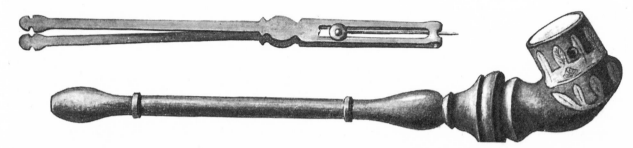

lecting the raw opium, a soft, sticky mass, which is exuded. The juice of some twenty thousand poppy capsules yields about 1 kg of opium. Chandoo, the prized smoking opium, is produced by complicated fermentation processes. After taking only a few puffs of chandoo from his bamboo pipe, the smoker enjoys a short, intoxicating feeling of well-being, followed by a state of semi-consciousness. This condition is accompanied by pleasant dreams, which are usually of an erotic nature. After it wears off, depression sets in, and with it the need, and finally the uncontrollable craving for another "fix"

The pure constituents of opium, in particular the main alkaloid morphine, are considerably more dangerous than chandoo. The German pharmacist Friedrich Wilhelm Sertürner succeeded in isolating the "sleep-inducing factor" from opium, the *principium somniferi*. Normal, healthy people feel hardly anything after

taking morphine; if anything, nausea and vomiting are often observed. Only repeated doses "elevate one above earthly existence", make the ugly beautiful, allow one to

forget injustice, physical and mental pain, and evoke pleasant dreams. The morphine-taker is eventually hooked, both mentally and physically, on the drug. In the advanced stages of addiction he suffers from insomnia, emaciation, trembling, impotence and mental disorders. It is then usually too late to halt his moral decline. The addict will stop at nothing, not even crime, to obtain the drug. If he stops taking it, in the first six to twelve hours he will suffer from deprivation symptoms that can prove fatal, ranging from vomiting, anxiety and depression to circulatory failure. Nonetheless, it is an astonishing fact that people engaged in intellectual and cultural work, despite years of addiction to morphine, have made considerable achievements.

Cardinal Richelieu, who was obliged on medical grounds to take a theriac containing opium (from 1546 on, this was an official medicament), became addicted to it. Charles Baudelaire, too, whom we already know to have been a "hashish eater", turned to opium after 1850. The French painter, novelist and film-director Jean Cocteau was also addicted to opium.

The composition of raw opium and its individual chemical components depend on the type of poppy and the area where it is grown. Opium from Asia Minor, for instance, contains more than twenty different alkaloids, derivatives of phenanthrene and benzylisoquinoline. The most important types of phenanthrene are morphine (11 to 17 percent), which is a strong painkiller and is highly addictive, codeine (0.5 to 3.5 percent), which is an antitussive, and thebaine (0.1 to 6 percent), which is a tetanic poison. The most important of the benzylisoquinoline structures is papaverine (0.1 to 2 percent), followed by narceine.

Morphine, codeine and papaverine are still used today in a large number of medicines. Pure morphine is used as a powerful painkiller because of its analgesic properties and soothing effect on the central nervous system. The fatal dose of morphine, taken orally, is about 200 to 400 mg. Death usually results from respiratory paralysis.

It is generally assumed that morphine interacts with neural transmission mechanisms of the central nervous system.

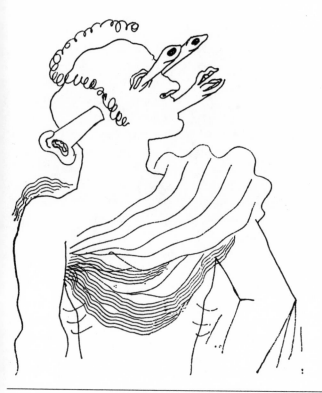

Many times more dangerous than morphine is its diacetylized derivative, heroin, which has shot to the top of the league table of addictive drugs in the USA in the last twenty or thirty years. In 1980 some two thousand people in New York alone died of an overdose; the fatal dose is only about 60 mg. Heroin is also claiming more and more victims every year in western Europe, for example in Great Britain and the Federal Republic of Germany. Sweden, the Netherlands and Italy also have a growing heroin problem, especially among the younger generation. Meanwhile, the heroin market has developed worldwide into a multi-million pound business for dealers. Police forces in the affected countries are almost powerless to stop them, because their narcotics squads are undermanned and have totally inadequate equipment and finance. Moreover, there is sufficient evidence to suggest that the "heroin mafia" must have friends in government departments and police headquarters in some countries.

Let us conclude our survey of narcotics in the narrower sense here, and turn to drugs which, even if not totally innocuous, are not such toxic poisons as those we have discussed in this chapter.

Extracts and distillates—*Stimulation from a cup.* One of the best-known stimulating extracts in the world is coffee, and its most effective, and therefore most important ingredient, caffeine. The product of the coffee tree (*Coffea arabica* and other cultivated varieties) from the family Rubiaceae can look back on an eventful history of praise and condemnation. The red, cherry-like fruit contains two kernels, the coffee beans, which obtain their characteristic aroma only after being roasted at 200 to 250° C. The beans contain about 1.5 percent of the stimulating alkaloid caffeine. Small quantities stimulate the heart, the metabolism and respiration, the blood pressure, body temperature and rate of blood circulation increase, and the blood vessels in the brain become dilated. This improved circulation of blood stimulates the organism, drives away weariness and temporarily improves performance.

Doctors today agree that, if drunk in moderation, coffee is harmless. People suffering from cardio-vascular instability, epilepsy, kidney disease, gout, high blood pressure or a tendency to arteriosclerosis should beware of frequent consumption, however. Healthy people whose intake of pure caffeine exceeds 500 mg will experience trembling of the hands, considerable excitement of the central nervous system, insomnia, palpitations and possibly angina pectoris. Caffeine is sometimes seen as a contributory factor in the development of stomach ulcers, because it stimulates gastric secretion, although the roasting of the beans may also play a part in this.

The lethal dose is fairly high; it is even possible to recover after consuming 5 g of pure caffeine. For a fatal dose, one would have to drink more than a hundred cups of strong coffee one after the other. Even Balzac and Voltaire did not achieve that, although according to contemporaries they drank up to sixty cups a day.

Quite a lot is now known about the biochemical effects of caffeine. It produces and releases increased quantities of noradrenalin in the brain and the peripheral sympathetic nerves. In addition, the effect of endogenous adrenalin and noradrenalin (i.e. which is produced in the organism) on the circulation and metabolism is stimulated. Caffeine also has a direct effect on the muscle fibres, which manifests itself particularly in increased contractions of the heart muscles.

Coffee has a very long history, which goes back to Biblical times—David is said to have seduced Abigail with coffee.

The last five hundred years in the history of coffee can be traced rather more precisely. In the 15th century, coffee came to Arabia from Abyssinia, and by the middle of the 16th century it was known in Constantinople, brought there by pilgrims, one suspects, returning from Mecca.

The Venetians, who knew coffee in about 1615, are thought to have brought it from Arabia to Europe. There is evidence to suggest that it was drunk in Marseilles in 1644, and in 1657 the world explorer Jean de Thévenot took it to Paris, where it was introduced to the Court of Louis XIV in 1669 by Sulaiman Agha, the envoy of Mahmud IV. What was probably the first public coffee-house in Paris was opened by two Armenians at the Saint-Germain fair in 1670. The first North German coffee-house was opened in Hamburg in 1670, and in the last quarter of the 17th century, such estab-

lishments increased rapidly in number throughout Europe. The first of the world-famous Viennese coffee-houses was opened in 1683, supposedly by a Pole called Kolscycki. His source of coffee was booty captured from the Turks, who had been routed by the German and Polish armies near Vienna shortly before. Legend has it that at first no-one knew what to do with these unfamiliar spoils, and that the coffee was thought to be camel feed.

In about 1700 the Dutch began to cultivate coffee in Java, and they were soon the leading European coffee dealers. The Dutch were faced with serious competition, however, when the French infantry officer Gabriel Mathieu De Clieux took the first coffee plants from the botanical gardens in Amsterdam and Paris to Martinique in the Lesser Antilles.

The history of the effects of coffee, too, has varied greatly over the centuries. There were times when it was blamed for numerous illnesses, but at the very least it was held responsible for impotence in men and a sagging bosom in women. The *Wiener Zeitschrift* wrote about this, the most harmless of all stimulants apart from tea, in its very first edition in 1896: "Constant and regular consumption of coffee will inevitably undermine even the strongest constitution and lead to actual coffee poisoning. The effects manifest themselves initially in a general irritation of the nerves, headaches, dizziness, buzzing in the ears and palpitations. These symptoms then disappear temporarily, and the symptoms of coffee dyspepsia, in other words digestive problems, start to appear. In more advanced stages of poisoning, the circulation is also affected. Sleeplessness, or very disturbed sleep with horrific nightmares, sudden terror and insuperable feelings of anxiety, causing profuse sweating, marked twitching of the limbs, lips and tongue, sometimes spreading to all of the facial muscles, are all symptoms which can be observed at this stage. The victim then goes downhill rapidly—his body

and intellect come closer and closer to complete collapse, ending in torpidity and insanity or, in some cases, in complete paralysis of the heart (an apoplectic fit)."

Coffee was often banned as the "Devil's brew", and coffee drinkers were threatened with draconian penalties. But its consumption has sometimes also been officially encouraged. This either happened in an attempt to reduce the consumption of spirits, or, as was the case under Frederick II of Prussia, to fill the state coffers by levying tax and duty on coffee. It was for this reason that the Prussian king made the coffee trade the monopoly of the state in 1781. We know that "Old Fritz" sent his "coffee-hounds" all over Prussia to catch illegal coffee roasters and impose heavy fines on them. Napoleon and other European rulers followed his example in later years. The excise duty levied on coffee is still a substantial source of revenue for the treasury today.

Before ending this short excursion into the world of coffee, let us look briefly at the chemistry of caffeine and its related purine derivatives.

In 1820 Friedlieb Ferdinand Runge, who is famous for his discovery of aniline in coal tar, was the first to isolate a crystalline coffee base from a sample of coffee given to him by Goethe. Two years later Pierre Joseph Pelletier, Pierre Jean Robiquet and Joseph-Bienaimé Caventou, all professors of pharmacy in Paris, described the active principle in coffee and called it caffeine. Another Frenchman, Jean Baptiste Oudry, discovered the active substance in black tea in 1827, naming it theine. Encouraged by Jöns Jakob Berzelius, Karl Jobst and Gerhardus Johannes Mulder proved in 1838 that the two substances were identical. In 1842 Alexandr Voskresensky, a Russian, discovered theobromine in cocoa; the beans contain up to 1.8 percent of this substance. Adolf Strecker succeeded in converting this into caffeine in 1861 by methylation, thereby proving the close structural relationship between the two substances.

In 1888 Albrecht Kossel discovered theophylline, a structural isomer of theobromine, in tea. In 1898 Emil Fischer finally discovered purine, the parent substance of the whole group.

Pure caffeine is an important ingredient of a number of medicines, in the treatment, for instance, of diseases of the heart and circulation, and as a synergetic compo-

nent of painkillers (analgesics). Many purine derivatives have been synthesized in recent times. Their differing effects enrich the range of medication available: even minor structural changes or variations in the functional groups have different biological effects.

Alongside the great community of coffee-drinkers there exists another, equally numerous, group of people who enjoy the quiet pleasure of a cup of tea. Black tea, along with beer, is one of the oldest drinks enjoyed throughout the world today; it probably originated in India. Tea was also drunk in China more than three thousand years ago. In A.D. 780 the Chinese poet Lu Yün wrote the first comprehensive work on the subject, *The Book of Tea (Chia Ching)*, in which he described the effects, properties and preparation of tea, and tea ceremonies. In Japan the Buddhist priest Bodhidharma was honoured from the 6th century on as the patron saint of tea. One of the many legends about him tells how, after many years of meditation, he broke his holy vow by being overcome by sleep. On wakening, he flew into such a rage about this that he cut off his eyebrows. They fell to the ground and sprouted as two tea plants. After he had eaten a few of their leaves, he felt fresh and invigorated. He told his pupils about the benefits of tea, and they then spread its popularity.

In the 16th century, knowledge of tea was brought to Europe by missionaries, travellers and Arab traders, and in the 17th century the Dutch and British East India Companies imported the first large quantities of dried tea-leaves from the Far East, and China in particular. As long ago as 1648, Philippe Silvestre Dufour praised the benefits of tea as follows: "One of the greatest benefits of tea is that it makes drunks sober again. It also cleanses the brain ..."

Tea reached Germany at the beginning of the 17th century, where it was initially sold by apothecaries as a medicament. It was soon drunk for pleasure, and became the subject of scientific treatises. In one of the first

of these, which appeared in Hamburg in 1634, called *Die naturgemässe Beschreibung der Caffee, Thee, und Chokolade, Tabacks mit Tractätlein* (On the nature of coffee, tea, chocolate and tobacco supplemented by a treatise), one reads about the tea that "each drink of it invigorates you and banishes sleep". But tea never be-

DISCOURSES

ON

T E A,

SUGAR,	SPIRITS,
MILK,	PUNCH,
MADE-WINES,	TOBACCO, &c.

WITH

PLAIN and USEFUL RULES

FOR

GOUTY PEOPLE.

By *THOMAS SHORT*, M.D.

LONDON:

Printed for T. LONGMAN, in *Pater-noster-row*; and A. MILLAR, in the *Strand*.

MDCCL.

Maté tea, or Paraguay tea, an alkaloid-rich stimulant whose popularity extended to Europe, especially in the 1930s, is obtained from the South American maté *(Ilex paraguariensis)*.

came established in Germany to the extent it did in England or Russia, for example; this is evident from pro capita consumption statistics.

As for the chemical data about tea, it contains much more caffeine than the coffee bean, with up to five percent (about two percent for black tea, and five percent for green), about twelve percent tannic acid, numerous vitamins (especially the growth vitamin B_1), essential oils and odoriferous substances, as well as chlorophyll, a number of mineral substances, and finally theophylline, which is a diuretic. The stimulating effect of tea affects the central nervous system for longer than coffee because of the influence of the theophylline and the essential oils. Coffee has a more powerful effect on the heart.

There are a number of other exotic plants which produce caffeine or very similar alkaloids, but let us consider only two examples here. The first of these is the maté *(Ilex paraguariensis)*, a three to six metre high South American evergreen tree. Its freshly cut branches are heated over an open fire at about 250 °C for just thirty or forty seconds to reduce its water content. The leaves are then stripped from the branches and roasted for several hours. After they have been chopped and stored, they can be used to make maté. General Francisco da Rocha Tailado said of it: "In the last phase of the Paraguay campaign ... I was a witness that our army was fed for 22 days almost exclusively on maté ..." Maté, which is also known as Paraguay tea, was also sold and enjoyed in Europe in the 1930s as a high-alkaloid stimulant (its active substance is caffeine), but the Second World War saw it pass into obscurity.

Maté became popular in Paraguay as early as the mid-16th century, when the Jesuit state was founded. The clerics discovered that with this drink they could wean the Guarani Indians off the alcohol to which slave traders had introduced them. They later realized that maté could be highly profitable, and by the second half of the 16th century they had secured themselves a trading monopoly. It was Aimé Goujaud (known as Bonpland), an army surgeon who accompanied Alexander von Humboldt on his South American expeditions, who was principally responsible for introducing the maté tree to other areas. Among other things, Bonpland was personal physician to Empress Joséphine and intendant of Malmaison. After the fall of Napoleon's empire and a period of exile in Uruguay, he was a prisoner of the dictator José Gaspar Rodríguez Francia for ten years. He eventually established large plantations and became the major producer of maté.

Extracts of the deadly nightshade *(Atropa belladonna)* were used in ancient times as a murder poison. They were also added to cosmetics and mediaeval magic ointments.

Even in ancient times, extracts of henbane (*Hyoscyamus* sp.) were used as poisons, stimulants and soporifics. The seeds in particular, when heated on hot iron plates or on coals, exude intoxicating vapours. They were also added to beer to make it more potent. Here the golden-yellow henbane, a variety of *Hyoscyamus niger*, is depicted.
From: *Der geöffnete Blumengarten*. Edited by August Johann G. Carl Batsch, Vol. 2, Plate 75. Weimar, 1798.

Black nightshade *(Solanum nigrum)*, after which the alkaloid-rich nightshade family is named.

Hyoscyamus aureus.

Portrait vessel of the Mochica culture. A priest wearing on his head the sacred narcotic mushroom Teonanácatl.
Peru, 5th to 8th century. Linden-Museum Stuttgart, Staatliches Museum für Völkerkunde.

The sacred Teonanácatl mushroom *(Psilocybe mexicana)*, from which an ancient Aztec narcotic is obtained, was worshipped in the form of stone sculptures even in pre-Mayan times (550 to 222 B.C.). Stone mushroom from Guatemala.
Staatliche Museen Preussischer Kulturbesitz, Museum für Völkerkunde, Berlin (West).

Indians eating hallucinogenic mushrooms.
From: *Codex Magliabecchiano* (detail). Facsimile, Rome, 1904.

Central European hemp *(Cannabis sativa)*.

A powerful narcotic, whose active substance is the famous mescaline, is obtained from the Mexican peyote cactus *(Lophophora williamsii)*.

The French poet Charles Baudelaire was seriously addicted to hashish.

Flower of the opium poppy *(Papaver somniferum)*.

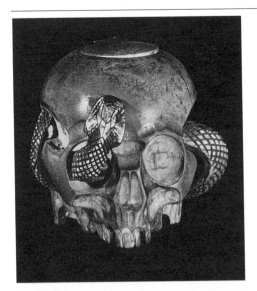

Opium box for storing the narcotic. Ivory. Dresden. In private ownership.

Opium and up to one hundred further ingredients were contained in the theriac, which was regarded for centuries as a panacea and universal antidote. Ingredients for the preparation of the divine theriac. Painting by an anonymous Master.
Historisches Museum, Museen der Stadt Hanau.

DISPENSATIO THERIACÆ CŒLESTIS à DÑO. J.D.
HOFFSTAD M.D. CONSIL. PAL. M. AULU M. 1693

The theriac was stored in valuable porcelain vessels, such as this richly decorated vase, crowned with sunflowers and wreaths in appliqué work, from Lunéville. Late 18th century. Pharmacie de l'Hôtel-Dieu, Mâcon (Saône-et-Loire).

Morphine addict in the slums of Paris, 1920s.

Visions on an LSD trip depicted by Heinz Trökes. The melting contours and preponderance of the brilliant colours is typical of paintings executed under the influence of drugs. Gallery R. P. Hartmann, Munich.

Following pages:
Opium smokers in a fashionable restaurant in Hong Kong, late 19th century.

Opium sellers in Persia.

Opium smokers in New York's Chinatown (1926).

In Japan the Buddhist priest Bodhidharma was worshipped as the patron saint of tea. Chinese scroll, c. 1600. Museum für Völkerkunde, Leipzig.

Grusinian women harvesting tea.

Coffee plantation in São Paulo State.

DEmnach der Allerdurchlauchtigſte/ Großmächtigſte König in Polen und Churfürſt zu Sachſen 2c. 2c. Unſer Allergnädigſter Herr 2c. auf erſtatteten allerunterthänigſten Bericht wegen derer Caffee-Häuſer und Billard-Spiele bey hieſiger Stadt in hohen Gnaden anbefohlen/ wie nachfolgender wahrer Abdruck mit mehrern beſaget:

Von GOttes Gnaden/ Friedrich Auguſtus/
König in Polen 2c. Hertzog zu Sachſen/ Jülich/ Cleve/ Berg/
Engern und Weſtphalen 2c. Chur-Fürſt/ 2c.

Jebe Getreue/ Wir haben Uns euern/ vom 31. Julii letzthin eingeſendeten allerunterthänigſten Bericht vortragen laſſen/ und daraus verleſen hören/ was ihr zu Abwendung derer vielen/ zeithero in denen Caffee-Häuſern und auf denen Billard-Spielen/ in der Stadt bey euch/ angemerckten und ausgeübten unfertigen Händel/ mit Schwelgen/ Spielen und andern dergleichen/ in ſieben unterſchiedenen Puncten zu verfügen/ unmaſsgeblich vorgeſchlagen/ und hierüber zu deſto mehrern benöthigten Nachdruck um Unſere Verordnung allergehorſambſt gebethen habet; Allermaſſen Uns nun euere/ diesfalls bezeigte gute Sorgfalt/ zu Verhütung allerhand ſolcher Exceſſe/ zu gnädigſtem Gefallen gereichet/ und wir/ euerm Vorſchlage nach/ das gantze Werck durchgehends hiermit approbiren und vor genehm halten; Als iſt hiermit Unſer Begehren/ ihr wollet ſolches durch einen öffentlichen gedruckten Anſchlag am Rathhauſe bey euch und ſonſten an Ort und Stellen/ wo nöthig/ ungeſäumt bekant machen/ darüber feſt und genau halten/ auch/ daß darwieder nicht gehandelt werden möge/ ſcharfſſe Uffſicht tragen/ und fleißig viſitiren laſſen/ wieder diejenigen auch/ ſo unſere Verordnung hierunter übertreten/ jedesmahl mit der darauff geſetzten Straffe verfahren/ übrigens aber/ die Auffrichtung mehrerer dergleichen Caffee-Häuſer und Billard-Spiele bey euch nicht verſtatten/ noch zulaſſen. Mochtens euch nicht bergen/ und geſchicht daran unſere Meynung. Datum Dreßden/ am 7. Auguſti, Anno 1716.

Unſern lieben Getreuen dem Rathe zu Leipzig.
præſ. den 12. Auguſt. 1716.

H. von Bünau.

Joh. Chriſtoph Günther.

Es wird von E. E. Hochw. Rathe dieſer Stadt ſolches hiermit jedermänniglich kund gemachet und krafft deſſelben verfüget/ daß diejenigen/ welchen von wohlgedachtem Rathe ein Caffee-Hauß oder Billard-Spiel zu haben erlaubet iſt/ wie denn ein jeder zuförderſt darumb anzuſuchen/ und den bis anhero angemaßten Schanck des Caffee und Billard-Spiels durch eine Conceſſion darzuthun/ ohne ſolche aber ſich deſſen bey Vermeidung ernſten Einſehens zu enthalten hat/ nachfolgende Puncte beobachten/ und darwieder in keine Wege handeln ſollen. 1.) Daß aller Auffenthalt und Bedienung von Weibs-Perſonen in Caffee-Häuſern/ ſo wohl bey Zurichtung des Getränckes und deſſen Auftragen/ als auch ſonſt unter was Vorwand es geſchehen möchte. 2.) Deßgleichen auch alle Würffel/ Karten und andere Glücks-Spiele/ den eintzigen Billard ausgenommen/ bey Straffe gegen den Caffee-Schencken zu exequiren/ gäntzlich verbothen ſeyn. 3.) Niemand Abends über 9. Uhr des Winters/ und 10. Uhr des Sommers bey 20. Thaler Straffe in ſolchen Häuſern geduldet/ und dieſelben über dieſe Zeit nicht offen gehalten. 4.) Die Kauff- und Handels-Jungen nicht zum Billard-Spiel gelaſſen. 5.) Um ein gewiſſes Quantum und nicht höher/ jedoch nach Beſchaffenheit und Condition derer/ ſo auf dem Billard ſpielen/ die Partie zu ſpielen geſtattet. 6.) Des Sonntags unter währendem Gottesdienſte keine Gäſte geſetzet/ und 7.) Wer in einem oder andern dieſer Puncte darwieder handeln würde/ das erſte mahl um 10. Rthlr. das andere um 20. Rthlr. geſtraffet/ das dritte mahl aber dieſer Nahrung gäntzlich verluſtig ſeyn/ dem Denuncianten der dritte Theil von der Geldſtraffe gefolget/ und deſſen Nahme verſchwiegen gehalten werden ſolle. Wornach ſich alſo allenthalben zu achten. Urkundlich mit dem gewöhnlichen Stadt-Secret bedrucket. Signatum Leipzig/ den 17. Auguſti 1716.

L. S.

Servant beer-brewer. Funeral offering from the tomb of an official of the Old Kingdom, Giza. Limestone, *c.* 2300 B.C.
Paelizaeus-Museum, Hildesheim.

The goddess of pulque, Mayauel, sits on a throne with an agave (Agavaceae) as a backrest. The stimulant pulque is obtained from the juice of the agave. Stone knife, hatchet and lance catapult may indicate that pulque was drunk as a stimulant before combat.
From *Codex Laud*.

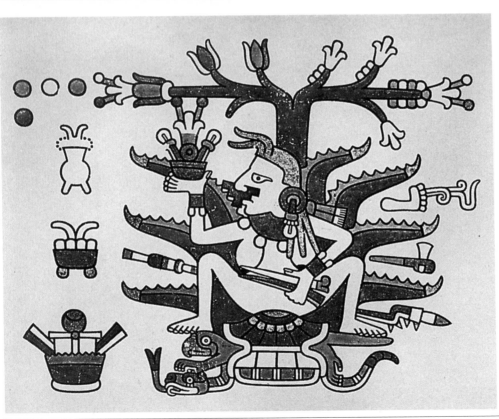

Silenus, the spirit of running water which spreads fertility, is usually depicted intoxicated by alcoholic beverages.
Anthony van Dyck, *Drunken Silenus*.
Gemäldegalerie Alte Meister, Staatliche Kunstsammlungen Dresden.

Ilya Efimovich Repin painted Modest P. Mussorgski in 1881, the year he died from the consequences of alcoholism. The clear signs of mental and physical decline are plainly visible in this portrait of the composer.
Tretyakov State Gallery, Moscow.

Workers on a Brazilian tobacco plantation.
After harvesting, the water content of the leaves is reduced by sixty percent by drying. They are then fermented.

Snuff-box owned by Frederick II, with the Prussian coat-of-arms and the king's initials. Enamel on copper. Germany, mid-18th century. Märkisches Museum, Berlin.

Tobacco-chewing was particularly popular among seafarers and in the coastal countries of northern Europe.
Pot for chewing tobacco. Stoneware, 2nd half of the 19th century. Stadtmuseum Schwedt/Oder.

The cola tree *(Cola acuminata)* flourishes in West Africa. Its nuts, which contain caffeine and theobromine, are used to make soft drinks, among other things.

Let us now turn to our second example of the lesser known exotic stimulants—the cola tree *(Cola acuminata)*, which grows in West Africa up to a height of twenty metres. It bears nuts which are sometimes white and sometimes red, the latter being particularly sought after, because they are richer in caffeine and contain one to two percent theobromine. The cola nut initially tastes bitter, but after a certain period of time its starchy constituents are converted into sugar, and it tastes sweet. It acts as a heart tonic, combats fatigue and suppresses the appetite.

The cola nut is still used today in the production of various soft drinks. In the Anglo-Saxon countries and the USA, the pro capita consumption of cola drinks—especially among young people—is thought to have equalled, and in some cases overtaken, that of coffee and tea during the 20th century. But cola surrogates and, unfortunately, an increasing number of alcoholic drinks such as rum and coke or vodka and coke are also significant here. This takes us on to our next chapter about drinking, where the emphasis shifts from the cup to the bottle or glass.

Stimulation from a bottle. The comforting memory of early childhood may be one reason for the very dramatic, and sometimes even fatal consequences for an increasing number of people when, in later life, alcohol in one of its many manifestations flows from the bottle instead of milk. Of all the alcoholic drinks, beer has been around the longest: it is the best-known throughout the world and, if enjoyed in moderation, is also the most relatively harmless for healthy people.

Probably the oldest surviving document on beer is the "Monument bleu" in the Louvre in Paris, which is hewn from stone and originated in the Sumerian Empire. It shows emmer, a type of wheat, being husked so that beer can be prepared as an offering to the goddess Ninharra.

Hammurabi, the great leader of the Babylonian Empire, did not omit to set down precise rules about the brewing and selling of beer, when he had the three hundred and sixty paragraphs of his code of laws engraved in stone. Anyone caught adulterating beer, for instance, was to be drowned in one of his own barrels, and the quality and price of the drink were strictly laid down.

Like so many other things, beer was known in ancient Egypt. Sculptures from the period around 2500 B.C. show the mash being kneaded. We know from ancient Egyptian papyrus scrolls that a queen received two and

a princess one jug of beer every day; officers, too, were entitled to two jugs of beer.

From Egypt the art of brewing spread by trade and warfare to West Africa (Abyssinia), Arabia and, finally, Europe. Although the Greeks and Romans were acquainted with beer, they preferred wine. The high-percentage spirits and liqueurs which are today the most popular alcoholic drinks, apart from beer, in Europe, have been produced only since the late Middle Ages. Today we have to face the fact that such concentrated types of alcohol have become the leading form of dangerous drug in most of the industrialized nations. The relatively low price of these drinks, their easy accessibility for all sections of the population, and the deliberate promotion of alcohol consumption through advertising and for tax revenue have made alcoholism an epidemic in our lifetime whose consequences cannot yet be predicted.

According to the World Health Organization (WHO), alcoholism is currently the third most frequent disease after heart and circulatory disease and cancer. The number of alcoholics receiving medical attention is about thirty million, but the real figure throughout the world is estimated at twice that number, nor should one forget that the WHO defines alcoholics only as those excessive drinkers whose dependence has reached the level where it is seriously affecting their physical and mental health, where it is resulting in conflict in their relationships with others, and where it is causing social and financial problems. The chronic alcoholic suffers from neurosis, psychosis, delirium, Korsakoff psychosis (characterized by very weak powers of perception and memory, as well as apathetic/euphoric or also anxious moods) and a permanent mental deficiency resulting from cerebral atrophy. The most advanced form of poisoning, alcoholic delirium, is a disease which can prove fatal. The symptoms are serious mental disorders, great anxiety and excitement, disorientation and

many optical hallucinations (such as the famous white mice). As vegetative symptoms such as trembling of the hands and arms also occur, this condition is known as delirium tremens.

Chronic alcohol consumption can also lead to diseases of the heart, kidneys and pancreas and to blood pressure disorders. Liver damage caused by alcohol and degeneration of the peripheral nervous system occur very frequently. Irreparable brain damage results, and the addict declines physically and morally in a quite disastrous way. He lives only to seek out alcohol, even in the form of cosmetics or cleaning agents which contain alcohol.

The suicide rate among alcoholics is about ten times higher than the average for the population as a whole.

The influence of alcohol on the children of alcoholics is a problem which has been discussed repeatedly. Even the Greeks were convinced of the evil consequences of alcohol consumption for their children, and they explained the misshapen form of the club-footed Vulcan by the fact that Zeus had fathered him while under the influence of drink. The philosopher Plato surmised that begetting children while intoxicated would result in feeble-minded, epileptic and sickly offspring.

Today we know that it is women who drink during pregnancy who are most likely to harm the foetus. According to American researchers, even light to moderate consumption of alcohol can result in a thirty to fifty percent likelihood of death or serious malformation of the embryo. We know today that the typical clinical alcohol syndrome in children takes the form of stunted growth at an early age, retarded mental development, anomalies of the head and face, defects of the extremities and malformations of the heart and genitalia.

The effect of alcohol cannot be explained in a few words, because biochemical and neurophysiological mechanisms interact in a number of different ways as the alcohol affects the body, and the drinker becomes dependent. Investigations in the seventies suggested that the primary waste product of alcohol, acetaldehyde, in all probability causes serious damage to the metabolism of the endogenous biogenic amines which serve the nervous system as neurotransmitters (which transmit nerve impulses). As this reaction takes place, it is believed that morphine structures are also created, which would explain the far-reaching similarities between the symptoms of morphine addiction and alcoholism. Habituation, dependency and withdrawal are remarkably similar with both drugs. However, to go into more detail at this point would be to digress too much.

A wide range of other ingredients in alcoholic drinks, such as fusel-oil in brandy and whisky or biogenic amines in wine, can also be harmful to the human organism, if taken in excess. In the case of fusel-oils, at least, animal experiments and epidemiological studies on selected sections of the population have shown that their presence in high-percentage alcoholic drinks is responsible for severe liver damage and for the development of malignant tumours ("alcoholics' cancer").

Stimulation with or without a mouthpiece.   We do not know how long man has been deriving pleasure from inhaling the smoke of leaves, flowers and seeds. But since smell and taste are among the primary senses, man must instinctively have connected "smell" with pleasure even before he was able to master fire, even if it was initially only the intoxicating scent of flowers or the exciting scent of the opposite sex which first prompted him to seek to increase his pleasure in what he inhaled.

Nicotine, the alkaloid contained in tobacco, must today be regarded as nothing less than a narcotic. Nicotine creates a form of toxicomania, tobacco addiction, which is very similar to typical drug addiction in terms of the dependency it creates. Heavy smokers usually have little success when they try to kick the habit.

The plant, which originally came from South America, is one of the two thousand two hundred species of alkaloid-rich nightshade plants (Solanaceae). *Nicotiana rustica* and *Nicotiana tabacum* are the species most frequently cultivated in Central and southern Europe. The leaves are harvested as soon as they start to turn yellow and exude their characteristic odour. The water content of the leaves is reduced by sixty percent by drying, and they are then fermented.

Rodrigo de Jerés and Luis de la Torre, two of Christopher Columbus's companions, were probably the first Europeans to come into contact with tobacco. They landed in Cuba on 28th October 1492, and gazed in wonder at the Indian natives who inhaled the smoke of glowing, rolled-up tobacco leaves through their nostrils. This discovery actually had disastrous consequences for Jerés, because when he returned to Seville the harsh Inquisitors threw him into jail as the first smoker, on the assumption that anyone who blew smoke out of his mouth must be in league with the Devil. But even the Church was unable to suppress the new vice of smoking. Increasing numbers of seafarers and conquistadores were led astray by the drug.

Hernán Cortés sent the first tobacco seed to Europe in 1508, to his king, Charles V. In about 1556 the French traveller André Thévet succeeded in cultivating the first tobacco plants in Charente. They then spread quickly throughout Europe, bearing a succession of new names connected with the history of tobacco, for example Peruvian henbane or ambassador's powder, Medici herb, old queen's herb, also called queen mother's herb or grand prior's herb. Some of these names probably

have their origins in the fact that the French envoy to Lisbon, Jean Nicot de Villemain, sent the first tobacco seeds to Catherine de Medici and the grand prior of France, Francis of Lorraine, in 1560. The name longest in use, Nicot's herb, and from it the term nicotine, were derived from this envoy's name. The first tobacco planter, André Thévet, was most indignant about this in his memoirs, and considered that he should have the right of giving his name to it.

After people had learned from the Indians how to inhale tobacco smoke, it soon became fashionable to take snuff; indeed, this habit reached epidemic proportions in the 17th to mid-18th centuries. In the Thirty Years'

the Crimean War (1853–1856) the English and French spread the habit all over Europe. With the trend towards mass production, cigarettes became the most popular form of tobacco consumption. Chewing tobacco was also widespread among sailors and in the coastal countries of northern Europe until *c.* 1900.

As was the case with coffee, the "prestige" of tobacco varied greatly throughout history. There were even times when it was considered a panacea and recommended in all possible forms, in poultices, powders and ointments, as a juice or as smoke. It also had its radical opponents, however, from a very early stage. James I of England banned tobacco without a second thought in 1603, saying that its "black, stinking smoke evokes the horrific image of an evil, bottomless hell". The Russian Tsar Mikhail Fedorovich Romanov went as far as to have the noses cut off users of snuff. Pope Urban VIII excommunicated smokers in 1621 on the grounds that they had sacrificed themselves to "a substance which degrades both body and soul". James I of England executed the afore-mentioned "importer" of pipe-smoking, Sir Walter

War, pipe-smoking began to compete with snuff. This custom is thought traditionally to have been brought to Europe from the North American colony of Virginia, which was founded in 1584, by Admiral Sir Walter Raleigh, a favourite of Queen Elizabeth I of England. The 19th century was the century of the cigar. The first German cigar factory was founded in 1788 by the Hamburg merchant Hans Heinz Schlottmann. In those days the cigar was definitely a symbol of the established bourgeois. Today cigarettes are predominant throughout the world. These are thought to have been "invented" in the Middle East in the 19th century. After

frequent use of tobacco shortens one's life). We cannot dispute this today, because the connection between cause and effect in terms of damage to health has scarcely been as well researched for any other drug as for smoking, which can cause diseases of the heart and circulation, gangrene and lung cancer.

The active substance which causes dependency, nicotine, was isolated in an impure form as "essence de tabac" by Louis-Nicolas Vauquelin in 1809; Christian Wilhelm Posselt and Karl Ludwig Reimann succeeded in isolating nicotine in 1828. They were decorated for their work by Grand Duke Louis of Baden. In 1843 Louis Henri Frédéric Melsens put forward the empirical formula for nicotine, but the structural formula was the work of Adolf Pinner (1893). Nicotine is a pyridine ring linked to an N-methylated pyrrolidine ring in the α-position to nitrogen. Tobacco also contains small amounts of various other alkaloids, however. Tobacco leaves can contain up to eight percent nicotine, and sometimes as much as sixteen percent. The leaves which are processed for commercial tobacco products normally contain between one and three percent of the alkaloid.

Raleigh, for alleged political conspiracy, and banned tobacco-smoking and snuff-taking by Act of Parliament, under pain of flogging and banishment from London. Sultan Murad IV had the hands and feet of offenders amputated, or even hanged them, and last but not least, the Persian Shah Abbas the Great resolved to burn tobacco dealers along with their wares.

Many prominent figures of more recent times have also been bitter opponents of the use of tobacco, including Johann Wolfgang von Goethe and Christoph Wilhelm Hufeland, the royal physician and director of the Charité hospital in Berlin. After a scientific dispute in 1699, Guy-Crescent Fagon, personal physician to Louis XIV, summarized his opinion as follows: "Ergo ex frequenti tabaci usu vita summa brevior" (Thus the

For non-smokers, the lethal dose of the highly toxic poison nicotine is about 40 to 60 mg, the quantity contained in only two or three cigarettes (although the smoker inhales only a small amount of this), or in 2 or 3 g of snuff. The toxic effect of nicotine is comparable with that of prussic acid.

How much nicotine is absorbed depends both qualitatively and quantitatively on the way the tobacco is consumed. Snuff-takers consume large amounts, but slowly, through the nasal mucous membranes, whereas in the case of tobacco chewing, equal amounts are absorbed through the mouth cavity and stomach. Puffing away at a pipe results in incomplete absorption, but this depends on the time the smoke remains in the mouth and nose. The greatest part of the nicotine contained in the smoke is absorbed by inhalation; this is particularly harmful because the liver, which has a detoxifying function, is by-passed, and nicotine reaches the heart and brain with each drag.

Nicotine is not the only harmful substance from which smokers are at risk. The smoke which they inhale is made up of gases and aerosols, and also contains a large number of low-molecular organic compounds such as alkanes, alcohols, ketones, esters, pyridine bases, etc., as well as small quantities of ammonia, hydrogen sulphide and prussic acid. Apart from the main active principle, nicotine, other gases are important when assessing the effects of smoking, in particular carbon monoxide, nitrogen oxide and a few irritant gases. Apart from benzopyrene and its derivatives, traces of nitrosamines and heavy metals such as chromium, arsenic, cadmium and vanadium have been found; all of these are carcinogenic.

But it is not just in smoke that nicotine can endanger life. Two examples will demonstrate this. In 1697 the writer Jean de Santeuil died of nicotine poisoning, after friends had spiked his wine with a few pinches of tobacco to make him more loquacious. Nicotine can also be deadly if it is absorbed through an open wound. We know of one case in which a tobacco processor from Höfen near Pforzheim in Germany died of nicotine poisoning a few hours after he gashed himself on a tobacco cutter.

In centuries past, the commission of crime has often contributed to our knowledge of toxicology, and of analytical toxicology in particular. In the case of nicotine, too, it was a murder which led to the first detection of the alkaloid in the human body. However, nicotine has only seldom been used as a murder weapon; because of its smell and taste, the victim must be forced to take it. Nevertheless, it has been used as a means of committing suicide, because in some countries it is, or once was, sold in the form of horticultural pesticides (to control the vine louse in viticulture, for instance). The annals of criminal history include the case of the nicotine murderer Count Hippolyte Visart de Bocarmé, who stood trial in 1851. He had lived in America for some years, and knew about the use of nicotine as an arrow poison. Bocarmé set up a laboratory in the wash-house of his castle, Bitromont, where he occupied himself with amateurish scientific experiments. It was here that he produced a "tobacco liquor" with which he poisoned his brother-in-law Gustave Fougnies to prevent his marriage, which threatened to deprive him of a legacy which he was expecting to inherit. To cover up his crime, he poured large quantities of wine vinegar into the mouth of his victim. When the examining magistrates and doctors saw the burnt face, mouth, mucosa and stomach of the dead man, they decided to send the intestines to Brussels for toxicological tests, where they were eventually examined by Jean-Servais Stas, a chemist at the military school there. He first established that the damage caused to the tissues could not be attributed to acetic acid alone, which led him to suspect that the vinegar was intended to conceal another poison. With the tenacity and training of a chemist, not to mention a certain amount of luck, he finally succeeded in isolating the poison from the body. He added a solution of potassium hydroxide and ether to an acidic aqueous alcoholic extract, and after evaporating the ether extract was left with a liquid with a characteristic smell and a bitter taste, which exhibited the typical reactions of the alkaloid. This complex process had thus enabled the chemist to isolate the alkaloid vegetable poison from the fats, proteins and carbohydrates of the human body. Even today, forensic chemists all over the world are familiar with the extraction method used by Stas (with some refinements by Friedrich Julius Otto). Stas had achieved what the pioneer of toxicology, Mathieu Joseph Bonaventure Orfila, had believed to be impossible. Vegetable poisons in the body were no longer undetectable. This discovery meant the death penalty for Bocarmé, who died by the guillotine.

Let us now retrace our steps to a specific form of tobacco consumption, namely chewing. This method of taking drugs is by no means restricted to tobacco. Let us consider two examples from non-European cultures which demonstrate this. One drug which is widely enjoyed in Southeast Asia is betel, which is produced by the betel palm *(Areca catechu)*, a tree which can reach up to 20 metres in height. The seeds of this tree are betel nuts, which are about the size of a hen's egg. Slices or pieces of these nuts are dusted with lime, wrapped in the leaves of the betel pepper *(Piper betle)* and chewed as quid. Apart from other areca alkaloids, the main alkaloid contained in betel nuts is arecoline, which is used as a vermifuge in veterinary medicine. The alkaloids were first described by Ernst Jahns in 1888. They are bonded to tannic acid in the plant. The physiological effect comes from the main alkaloid, which is an N-methyl tetrahydronicotinic acid dimethylester and the saponified product arecaidine. Arecoline acts similarly to the neurotransmitter acetylcholine, the substance which is responsible for transmitting impulses between individual nerve-endings.

Occasional betel-chewing is relatively harmless, but in the long term it can cause loss of appetite, impaired digestion and permanent weakness in the entire organism. The tannic acid also occasions inflammation of the gums, and sometimes the mucous membranes peel off. Recent experiments also revealed that betel alkaloids can promote, or even cause, the development of oral carcinoma (betel cancer). This drug was also

known under a wide variety of names in ancient times; it was described, among others, by the Greek philosopher Theophrastus in 340 B.C. Today more than two hundred and fifty million people are thought still to use it. Betel is enjoyed over an area of some ten million square kilometres, from the coast of East Africa to New Guinea, although its main centre has always been southern India, from Sri Lanka to the Malabar coast. Betel was, and still is, highly prized in other parts of southern Asia, too. Marco Polo, the great 13th-century explorer of Asia, told of betel chewers in Burma, Thailand, Cambodia, Vietnam and on the south coast of China. It is also popular in the Pacific islands, from the Philippines and Indonesia to the Molucca,

Caroline, Mariana and Fiji Islands. In some areas betel is so important that the distance to the next village is given in "quid lengths". In certain regions betel-chewing is still a sign of wealth, and the respect of the natives is commanded by those with bulges in their cheeks caused by a quid, rings of lime on their black teeth and a bountiful supply of red spittle. Indeed, in the Philippines the young Tagalog girls only consider the marriage proposals of a suitor who can prove his ardour by whipping the betel quid out of the mouth of his intended with one flick of the tongue.

It is typical of yet another substance that it is chewed in the same way as the harmless and now commonplace chewing gum. The fresh leaves and buds of kat *(Catha edulis)*, a shrub of the Celastracea family, have been known for much longer than coffee in Arabia and East Africa. Its leaves are chewed either fresh or dried like tobacco, but it is also possible to prepare a sort of tea from them (Arabian tea). It causes euphoria, stimulation, loss of appetite and fatigue. It was sometimes kat alone which kept the Somali going during military campaigns.

Addicts of the drug become highly-strung, very susceptible to disease and, if denied access to the drug, emaciated. As with betel, chewing chat is symbolic of wealth in some areas. One negative property is its powerful antiaphrodisiac effect, in other words it suppresses the sex drive, and for this reason many women in Yemen refuse to marry men who chew kat.

To the best of our present knowledge, the main active alkaloid appears to be cathinine, and α-amino-propiophenone, which dimerizes very readily in the presence of oxygen. For a long time it was thought that cathine (d-norpseudoephedrine), which was discovered by Albert Beitter in 1901, but which is present only in low concentrations, was the most important active principle. Apart from this, more than forty other alkaloids as well as other constituents of various structural types

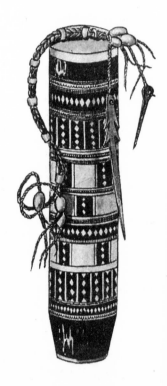

have been identified. This example indicates once again how the chemistry of natural products still has a long way to go if we are to gain a better insight into toxicological processes.

We should not leave this field of harmless and dangerous stimulants and drugs without first mentioning substances which are not initially connected in the minds of the general public with intoxication and stimulation. And yet the substances which we are going to consider here are representative of many more which have often enough posed problems for toxicologists as well as forensic experts and social workers.

One of these is camphor. In earlier times it was a highly-prized commodity, and was often demanded from vanquished peoples as a war tribute. Camphor was considered a valuable gift when credentials were presented, or on other similar occasions. For example, the Chinese emperor sent a casket of the substance to Pope Benedict VII in 1345. In the 12th century Abbess Hildegard of Bingen advised her nuns to take camphor so that they could follow Mass more attentively. It was long thought to be not only a mental stimulant, but also to offer protection against cholera, and even at the end of the 19th century the chemist François-Vincent Raspail regarded camphor as the much-desired cure-all. Camphor is a ketone belonging to the monoterpene group, and is produced by steam distillation from shavings of the East Indian camphor laurel *(Cinnamomum camphora)*. Small quantities of it are also contained in the essential oils of other plants—such as sage, valerian and peppermint. It is hardly surprising that camphor addiction has joined company with the many other types of addiction over the centuries. It was particularly rife in Britain, Slovakia and, in the 19th century, among Central European immigrants to the USA. The reasons for this are unknown, unless it was the modest price of camphor in comparison with other addictive drugs. Doses of between 0.5 and 3 g were generally taken in milk or alcohol, or in tablet form. At the end of the 19th century, Louis Lewin described camphor intoxication as stimulating the intellect and diffusing a warm feeling over the skin. The effects lasted for about an hour and a half.

Large doses of the drug cause pronounced restlessness and a "hurricane of thoughts", making the victim incapable of any mental work at all. There is also temporary amnesia and disorientation. Camphor is still used in medicine as a heart stimulant and in ointments. Oils containing camphor serve as homoeopathic cures for diseases of the respiratory tract.

The inhaling and drinking of ether also gained a certain degree of popularity in the mid-19th century, particularly in Ireland, but also in the Memel territory, Galicia, Norway and parts of Russia. Some Irish peasants are thought to have drunk up to 400 g of ether every day. It is almost impossible to cure this addiction, because serious withdrawal symptoms, similar to those found with morphine addiction, occur. The French writer Guy de Maupassant, after experimenting with various drugs, finally became addicted to ether. In his letters he describes the consequences of chronic consumption as delirium, hallucinations, anxiety and unbearable migraine attacks.

Many other solvents have also been used for stimulation. Richard Wagner was not alone in drinking and inhaling perfume; the growing popularity of luxury perfume is particularly marked in our times. Of course, pleasant and stimulating scents are good business today, as they always have been. Scientists have made thorough investigations of their beneficial potential. But we are now being diverted into the realm of stimulants with no toxicological significance. The reader must be left to examine this area himself if the opportunity arises.

To conclude this chapter on stimulants and drugs, let us address a few words to chemical simulations of natural materials.

In the 1930s chemists met with the first signs of success in their attempts to synthesize stimulants and pep pills. This work was inspired mainly by examinations of the alkaloid phenylmethylamine propanol found in the shrubby horsetail or sea-grape *(Ephedra vulgaris)*. The Chinese used the sea-grape as a cure for asthma five thousand years ago. The first synthetic amphetamine was Benzedrine (β-phenylisopropylamine), which was produced by George Barger and Henry Hallet Dale, and was the subject of intensive research in the USA in the 1930s. It was soon being produced all over Europe under many different names. In the late thirties methylamphetamine (Pervitin) stood at the forefront of research in Germany. The Second World War led to a much wider distribution of this type of stimulant. English and American airmen in particular are thought to have taken considerable quantities of Benzedrine. After the war, all sorts of different people began to use stimulants; sportsmen, students, long-distance truck drivers and many others. As these can become addictive, they lie on the borderline of narcotics. Side-effects such as hallucinatory delirium, psychomotorial excitement and loss of appetite have sometimes been observed. In the opinion of Japanese researchers, the use of amphetamines increases human aggressiveness: this conclusion was partly based on the fact that of sixty murderers arrested in Tokyo in the months of May and June 1954, thirty-one had used stimulants of this type.

In the mid-sixties reports of potent cocktails hit the headlines in Western newspapers. These mixtures of amphetamines and alcohol were being taken by young people in discotheques and elsewhere to achieve a state of euphoria. In most countries, preparations containing amphetamines are considered addictive and are available only on prescription. The pharmacological effects of these derivatives of phenylalkylamine are the release of noradrenalin from the adrenergic nerve endings and increased activity of the central nervous system, which takes the form of heightened physical and motorial reactions and an improvement of associative and intellectual abilities. Nowadays different substances are being mixed with alcohol in the discotheques—however, this is the field of drug abuse and cannot be discussed here. This brings us to the end of our chapter on human weaknesses, passions and addictions to popular, and also less harmful stimulants. The following chapters will show that there are many other, often much more dramatic, ways of achieving stimulation, and that it is with good reason that the skull and crossbones is sometimes depicted on the labels of bottles and jars containing animal, vegetable or mineral poisons, or poisons produced in large-scale chemical plants.

Fungi

(Fungal poisons, poisonous fungi, microbial poisons)

Poisonous mushrooms and toadstools. There is room here to describe only a few of the poisonous mushrooms and toadstools which can be found in the woods and meadows. These might just as well be called the "classic" toxic fungi, arguably the most poisonous of their kind.

Some one hundred species of poisonous mushrooms and toadstools are indigenous to the northern temperate zone; nearly forty of these are thought to endanger life, and ten of them are deadly. Most of the latter belong to the genus *Amanita*.

The most dangerous toadstool in Central Europe is the aptly-named death cap *(Amanita phalloides)* and its white variety *Amanita verna*. In North America the most dangerous are the white species *Amanita tenuifolia*, *Amanita bisporigera* and *Amanita virosa*, which are known as the "destroying angel". The death cap flourishes from July to October, preferably under oak or beech trees or in meadows. Despite numerous attempts to educate the public, frequent cases of it being eaten in ignorance still occur. It is confused mainly with the firwood agaric *(Tricholoma auratum)* and the russula *(Russula sp.)*.

About ninety-five percent of all cases of toadstool poisoning in Central Europe are caused by the death cap, of which thirty to forty percent are fatal. A single toadstool contains enough poison to kill two or three people.

Serious research into the chemistry of this poison began in the USA at the start of the 20th century. Even then, scientists were able to distinguish between haemolytic phallin, which had been described previously, and which is heat-sensitive, and other toxins, which cannot be destroyed by cooking. The compound now known as phallolysin is a polymolecular proteinaceous substance, which is denatured during heating, so it is not poisonous if cooked or fried. This type of haemolysin is found in a wide range of fungi.

In 1937 the first heat-resistant toxin was isolated in crystalline form by Feodor Lynen and Ulrich Wieland in Münster; they named it phalloidin. We have since discovered that this poison cannot really be solely responsible for the characteristic toxic effect, firstly because only a small quantity can be absorbed by the gastro-intestinal tract, and secondly because its concentration in the toadstool is not enough to kill a man, even if it is the main constituent. We know that it is one of a group of bicyclic peptides containing seven amino acids, which damages the endoplasmic reticulum of the liver. The LD_{50} value for mice, i.e. the concentration at which there is a fifty percent mortality rate, is about 2 mg/kg. It is phalloidin which is mainly responsible for the initial symptoms of poisoning, such as painful, convulsive vomiting, long periods of diarrhoea and extreme dehydration.

Amanitine, which is slow-working but lethal, was isolated in crystalline form in 1940 by Heinrich Wieland and his colleagues. It later transpired that this so-called α-amanitine was only one of several very similar bicyclic octapeptides (containing eight amino acids). Such amanitines are about twenty times more toxic than phalloidin. They attack the cell nuclei directly, causing severe damage to the liver in particular (leading to painful enlargement of the liver, jaundice and coma hepaticum). Failure to urinate (anuria) and uremia are later symptoms of poisoning. The fatal dose of these toxins for man is about 0.1 mg/kg.

Theodor Wieland developed an interesting and very simple test for these amanitines which can be carried out even by a layman. Press a freshly cut piece of the fungus firmly onto the unprinted edge of a newspaper until a damp patch is formed, then let this dry naturally. If the patch is moistened with six to eight millilitres of ordinary hydrochloric acid, then a blue colour will appear within five to ten minutes if more than 0.02 mg of the poison is contained in 1 ml of the solution. The ac-

The natural-product chemist Bernhard Witkop, who lives in Bethesda (Maryland), described this historical picture as "Trypto-fantasies", because toad poisons contain basic derivatives of 5-hydroxy-tryptophan: the active substance of the toxic amanitines found in Amanitae is the rare 6-hydroxy-tryptophan.

tual quantity of amanitines in one toadstool is about five to ten times as great, however. (The discolouration is caused by a chemical reaction between the amanitines, the hydrochloric acid and the pine lignin contained in the newspaper.)

One edible toadstool which enjoyed a long period of great popularity, and which often shoots up in large numbers during the spring, is the false morel or lorchel (*Gyromitra esculenta*). For a long time, it was exported profitably by Poland. During the 19th century, however, cases of serious, and even fatal, poisoning occurred, although these were originally ascribed, inter alia, to incorrect preparation and to the use of copper cooking utensils. In 1882 it was proved that this toadstool contains a toxin which can, under certain circumstances, be lethal. In 1885 helvolic acid was isolated from the false morel, and this was regarded as the toxic principle for many years. It was not until 1967 that chemists discovered the nitrogenous toxin gyromitrin, whose effect is similar to that of the constituents of the death cap. Most of the poison can be extracted by cooking for ten minutes, but nonetheless, no more than 500 g of the toadstool should be eaten within twenty-four hours. The important thing to remember is that the poisonous effect of the false morel cannot be predicted with absolute certainty; it depends, for instance, on how old the specimen is, and where it is found. In addition, different people vary quite considerably in their sensitivity to the poison; a phenomenon which is quite often observed with natural toxins.

The ink cap (*Coprinus atramentarius*) is an interesting toxicological and pharmacological curiosity. Although it is edible, it causes a temporary hypersensitivity to alcohol. After eating the fungus, one or two bottles of beer will suffice to produce symptoms such as flushing of the face, irritability and numbness of the extremities, acceleration of the pulse rate, nausea and vomiting. This is due to the coprin which produces a strong acetal-

dehyde-dehydrogenase inhibitor in vivo 1-hydroxy-cyclopropylamine, thus retarding the catabolism of the primary alcoholic metabolite acetaldehyde. Hypersensitivity to alcohol is also apparent in a number of synthetic chemicals of a completely different structural type. The example we have known about for longest is calcium cyanamide.

Cases of fly agaric (*Amanita muscaria*) poisoning are extremely rare in Central Europe, because the bright red cap with its white spots is recognized by almost everyone as a by-word for poison. It is therefore hardly ever confused with non-poisonous toadstools. But the situation is different elsewhere. In Italy, for instance, where the edible golden agaric or imperial mushroom (*Amanita caesarea*) is common; this bears a superficial resemblance to the fly agaric.

The best-known active substance in the fly agaric is the alkaloid muscarine, which was first isolated by Johann Ernst Oswald Schmiedeberg and his colleagues in 1864, although only in impure form. The symptoms of poisoning are very complex and resemble those which are caused by poisons that attack the central nervous system.

One to three hours after eating the toadstool, agitation, confusion, unmotivated laughter and hallucinations are observed. In serious cases, maniacal fury can also develop. This is followed by extreme exhaustion, paralysis and loss of consciousness. On closer examination, these symptoms cannot be attributed to muscarine, because the fresh toadstools contain only about 0.0002 percent of the substance, while a number of other toadstools which cause symptoms which differ fundamentally from those of the fly agaric contain much higher quantities of muscarine. The red-staining inocybe (Inocybe patouillardii), for instance, contains twenty times as much. So the devil's boletus (Boletus satanas), the poisonous false champignon (Clitocybe rivulosa) and the panther mushroom (Amanita pantherina) also contain higher concentrations of muscarine.

The psychoactive effect is now thought to be caused by the constituents ibotenic acid, muscimol and muscazone. The fly agaric is so called because in days gone by, slices of the toadstool were placed in sugared milk as a fly trap; we do not yet know why this was done, although muscimol and ibotenic acid do have some insecticidal properties.

The symptoms described here indicate a possible link with narcotics. In the ancient Indian Rigveda, the toadstool known as the soma, from which narcotics can be extracted, is worshipped as a deity. It is also known from legends that the ancient Norwegian berserkers ate small quantities of toadstools for the purpose of intoxication. There is also proof of similar activity in northeastern Siberia. As these poisoning symptoms were often linked with attacks of blind fury, the expression "to go berserk" entered the language. The Nordic peoples even used the very rare fly agaric as a form of payment for reindeer. Extracts of the toadstool were mixed with the juice of the whortleberry (Vaccinium uliginosum), a member of the family Ericaceae, and prepared in such a way as to cause hallucinations and confusion. Even the urine of a person using this drug is psychoactively effective, and was used to extend the period of intoxication in areas where few of these toadstools could be found.

We have already touched on some of the fungi with a genuine psychotropic effect on man in the chapter about narcotics. This illustrates once again how difficult and therefore arbitrary it is to assign poisons to particular groups.

Some species of mushroom have also been used occasionally for medicinal purposes. So for instance, the touchwood (Fomes fomentarius), which was used to make tinder before the invention of matches, was placed on wounds to stop bleeding in days gone by.

Even in the 20th century, the purging agaric (Fomes officinalis) has been administered as a powerful laxative, for asthma and coughs and to prevent night sweats. Jew's ear (Auricularia auricula) marinated in wine was formerly prized as a cure for dropsy and throat infections. In 1975 the Chinese harvested 5700 tons of these fungi to use as painkillers and styptics, against uterine haemorrhage, haemorrhoids, stomach-ache and toothache. In some areas of the Caucasus and the Ukraine, ingredients are extracted from the carrion fungus (Phallus impudicus) for an ointment to cure gout and rheumatism, while a relative of the carrion fungus is still cultivated in Asia for the powerful anti-inflammatory substances it produces.

The shiitake (Lentinus edodes), a fungus which is cultivated in Japan and China, is thought to prevent circulatory disease by reducing the amount of cholesterol in the blood. Some 130,000 tons are produced in Asia every year. Closer examination of its constituents in Japan led to the discovery of several polysaccharides, which have been shown in animal experiments to inhibit the growth of tumours.

There may be a sound basis to some of these cures, which can be explained by the presence of biologically active constituents, but others strike one as extremely fanciful. For example, it used to be thought that dog bites would heal better if slices of the edible boletus were placed on the wound; these were also supposed to remove freckles and birthmarks. In Asia a paste of pulverized larch agaric and vinegar is spread over wounds caused by venomous snake bites, and this toadstool was formerly used in Europe in a similar way for animal bites. So far no plausible biochemical explanation has been found for these applications of fungi.

The life work of the German chemists Heinrich Wieland and his son Theodor demonstrates quite clearly the important secrets which can be discovered in the world of fungi, and how much toxicology can be enriched by natural-product chemistry.

The concept of fungi is, however, much more far-reaching than is commonly assumed. In common parlance the term "fungus" is often taken to refer only to mushrooms and toadstools which are visible as individual specimens, but this fails to take the microscopic world of fungi into account.

Poison from microfungi and microorganisms.
Under certain circumstances, microfungi can become established in foodstuffs and animal feed, where they produce mycotoxins, poisons which can be very dangerous to both man and beast. Many facts and legends have been woven around ergot *(Claviceps purpurea)*, a fungus which grows most commonly on ears of rye. In the early Middle Ages, in particular, epidemics of ergot poisoning were rife in Central Europe. This fungus was first described in detail in the herbal of Adam Lonitzer, a Frankfurt physician, in 1582. In 1630 the Frenchman Tuillier was able to prove, by experimenting with the feed of his hens, that rye contaminated by ergot was responsible for disease. In Germany it was Johann Taube, physician at the Hanoverian Court, who in 1771 recognized the importance of fungus for this type of poisoning, which was known as ergotism. This poison

manifested itself in two different ways. In Germany, it took the form mainly of convulsive ergotism, an attack on the nervous system which began with itching of the limbs, known as St. John's Dance. The main symptoms of the disease were painful, convulsive muscle contractions, which finally became epileptic in nature. The limbs sometimes remained twisted in abnormal positions. It was generally the poorer sections of society who prepared their staple food of bread from unwashed grain, who were particularly affected. Ergotism only diminished in the 18th century, when Frederick the Great

began to import potatoes, and legal provisions were made for the thorough washing of grain.

The other way in which ergotism manifested itself centred mainly on France, whose inhabitants suffered from the gangrenous form, otherwise known as "St. Anthony's fire" or "holy fire". The peripheral blood vessels suffered serious damage, whole parts of the body died off, and the blue-black mummified toes, arms or legs could be detached from the body without any bleeding. Over the centuries, many people afflicted with this terrible disease undertook a pilgrimage to Saint Didier in the Dauphiné, to visit the relics of St. Anthony the Great. A lay brotherhood eventually assumed responsibility for the care and provisioning of many pilgrims. This brotherhood developed into the Order of St. Anthony, one of whose duties was to tend victims of St. Anthony's Fire. Ergotism has even influenced the outcome of wars. In 1772, twenty thousand men which had been amassed to drive the Turks from the Black Sea and gain access to the Mediterranean are said to have been carried off by it; they formed part of the army of Peter the Great.

But mass poisoning has occurred even in the most recent past. In 1951 three hundred people were affected by ergotism in Limoges in southern France, and five of these died. Investigations by the French health authorities led to a court case which revealed that a baker had used flour contaminated with ergotism which he had purchased on the rural black market.

At a very early stage, a completely different effect of ergotism was also recognized. Lonitzer's herbal related that midwives had used the drug since time immemorial as an oxytocic. In 1808 the work of the US doctor John Stearns secured a place for ergot in official medicine, but its use in obstetrics remained very controversial. Success and failure stood side by side: the latter took the form principally of an increase in child mortality. The reason for this was the different composition of active ingredients in the various varieties of ergot. This provided a stimulus for research into the isolation and structural analysis of the active principles. In 1918 Arthur Stoll finally succeeded in isolating the most important alkaloid constituent, ergotamine, in the Sandoz laboratories. It is extremely toxic but very valuable for pharmaceutical purposes.

Die
Geschichte
der
Kriebel-Krankheit
besonders derjenigen
welche
in den Jahren 1770 und 1771
in
den Zellischen Gegenden
gewütet hat
beschrieben
von
Johann Taube
Hofmedicus, Mitglied der Königlichen Landwirthschaft Gesellschaft zu Celle und Correspondent der Königlichen Gesellschaft der Wissenschaften zu Göttingen.

Göttingen,
bey Johann Christian Dieterich, 1782.

Some twelve fungal toxins with a wide variety of medicinal applications are currently known; ergotamine preparations, for instance, can be used to treat migraine, but are also used in modified form to alleviate labour-pains.

Since the early 1960s, a number of moulds have also been the subject of toxicological research, because many species are extremely useful aids to the production of high-quality foodstuffs, including various cheeses—e.g. Camembert, Roquefort and other veined cheeses. The fungus *Botrytis cinerea* is used to aromatize particularly fine wines, and there are other possible uses, too, for these and other moulds. In recent years an entire biotechnological industry has developed around the use of microbial agents.

The often life-saving antibiotic penicillin is also the product of a mould *(Penicillium notatum)*. As its name suggests, an antibiotic is a "substance acting against life", a poison which, in this particular case, is able to kill microbes.

Apart from these useful moulds, there are many others which produce mycotoxins, which are very poisonous to man and beast alike. So many of these are now known that we will have to confine ourselves here to their most toxic representative, *Aspergillus flavus*. It produces the highly-toxic aflatoxins, and flourishes most commonly on peanuts, cheese, and grain products. The fungus was only discovered when one hundred thousand turkeys perished of a mysterious disease (known as turkey X disease) in Great Britain in the early sixties. Post-mortem examinations revealed serious haemorrhaging and other damage to the liver in all birds. The poisoning was eventually traced back to the feed, which was very mouldy Brazilian peanut meal containing aflatoxins. The chemical structure of the most important aflatoxins was discovered in 1965. Today we know of more than twenty-five moulds which produce these substances. These are mainly species of *Aspergillus* and *Penicillium*, which can flourish on a wide variety of foodstuffs. Aflatoxins are a group of substances with differing chemical structures, invariably with fused oxygenic rings which contain the structural element of the coumarins.

The particular threat presented by the aflatoxins lies in their ability to spread through foodstuffs, so that it is not only the superficial mouldy patch which is dangerous, but also the levels further down which do not appear to be affected. For this reason, mouldy bread should always be thrown away. Aflatoxins are not only acutely toxic, as was demonstrated by the decimation of the British turkeys; they are also extremely carcinogenic. The dangers of acute poisoning are not so serious for man, because very mouldy food is unlikely to be consumed, and the lethal dose of aflatoxins is as high as 1 to 7 mg/kg. The main problem for human health is the long-term damage, which usually takes the form of cancer. Aflatoxin B_1 is one of the most powerful carcinogenic substances known today, and about seventy-five times as powerful in this respect as dimethylnitrosamine. As little as 10 µg of aflatoxin B_1 results in

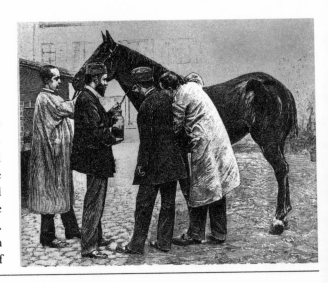

cancer of the liver in one hundred percent of cases in- volving rats. For humans too, the consumption of mouldy peanuts and grain can be linked to a significant increase in cancer of the liver because of the aflatoxin

content. Of every one hundred thousand people who contract primary hepatic cancer, 0.18 are Danes, 1.7 white North Americans, but 14 Bantus and 25 to 30 male inhabitants of the Imhambane district as well as 98 male members of the Shangana tribe (Moçambique) because their diet consists mainly of peanuts and other foodstuffs which are susceptible to mould. A random test in Moçambique revealed that ten percent of foodstuffs were contaminated by aflatoxins. On the other hand, primary hepatic cancer is extremely rare in the arid regions of North Africa, where conditions are very unfavourable for the growth of moulds.

It is interesting to note that the natives of former British Guiana disposed of those who fell foul of them with a poisonous drink made of peanuts contaminated with aflatoxins.

At this point a little more needs to be said about mi- croorganisms in their capacity as producers of poison, because their functions and effects in nature are ex- tremely diverse. Many bacteria and fungi play a key role in the natural cycle. They can be very dangerous to man, for example by causing infectious diseases or, and this is particularly relevant to us here, by producing poisonous metabolites (exotoxins, such as the bac- terium *Clostridium botulinum*, staphylococci and the moulds mentioned above) or internal toxins (endotox- ins), which are released in the human organism, such as salmonella toxins or those of the bacterium *Clostridium perfringens*.

The most common cases of bacterial food-poisoning are caused by the enterotoxins of the staphylococci. These cause severe vomiting and diarrhoea which, in a few cases, are accompanied by circulatory failure. If staphylococci come into direct contact with food with a high protein or carbohydrate content (e.g. from sup- purating wounds, nasal mucous, etc.), they can multi- ply rapidly on this breeding ground. About one to six hours after affected food is eaten, the symptoms de- scribed above will be observed. The toxins are pro- teinaceous substances with a molecular weight of 15 to 25,000. They are not destroyed by heat.

Salmonellae are bacteria which form endotoxins; after six to forty-eight hours they may cause enteritis, sometimes accompanied by fever, vomiting and diar- rhoea. In extremely rare cases, they can even be lethal. Unlike the proteins described above, these poisons are destroyed by heat.

The most lethal types of food poisoning, however, are caused by the botulinus toxins produced by the bac- terium *Clostridium botulinum*, which is found all over the world, even in street dust and soil. Fortunately this is extremely rare nowadays. These bacteria thrive par- ticularly well in protein-rich environments, but also in vegetable preserves. Such preserves as well as other vacuum-packed foodstuffs, are particularly at risk, be- cause these bacteria can exist even in an oxygen-free en- vironment. Modern packaging methods, such as the use of autoclaves, kill off the germs. For this reason, not a single case of botulism has occurred in the USA since 1925 as a result of eating canned produce, although some twenty thousand million cans are produced every year. Danger sometimes lurks, however, in fruit and vegetable preserves which have been prepared at home, or in other foodstuffs. Six hundred cases of this type of food poisoning were recorded in the Federal Republic of

Germany between 1962 and 1973, thirty of which were fatal.

In Massachusetts a woman is thought to have died from the results of licking her finger after opening a preserving jar contaminated by the botulinus toxin.

Exotoxins (metabolic secretions of the bacterial cell) cause nausea, double vision, difficulty in swallowing and speaking, and paralysis of the bladder and intestine after about twelve hours, or sometimes even longer; finally, respiratory paralysis causes death. The toxin paralyzes the nerve endings, so that the approaching nervous impulse cannot release any more acetylcholine, thus effectively blocking the nerve impulses. When poisoning occurs, there is no way of preventing or counteracting this paralysis.

Today we know of various strains of *Clostridium botulinum*, which produce six different poisons. They differ in terms of toxicity, but not in the way in which they work. These toxins are considered to be among the most powerful substances existing in nature. In chemical terms, they are globulin proteins with a high molecular weight. Botulinus toxin type A, for instance, has a molecular weight of about one million. The lethal dose, taken orally, is only 10 μg. Most poisonous of all is type B, which in experiments on mice killed fifty percent of the animals with a dose of 0.000002 μg/kg. The specialist literature gives the lethal dose of this botulinus toxin for humans as about 0.1 μg.

The active substance in botulinus was considered for use as a chemical weapon in some countries during and after the Second World War. It was calculated that 30 g of the pure poison would be enough to kill about two hundred million people. The international ban on biological weapons agreed by the UN in 1972 also covered toxins of this type.

Bacterial poisons are also responsible for diseases such as tetanus, amoebic dysentry, cholera and diphtheria, which were such scourges in former times.

From 1735 a terrible epidemic raged through the colonies of New England, to which some twenty percent of all young children had succumbed by 1740. The symptoms were a burning fever, a very sore throat and eventually tissue damage to the internal organs. After the bacterium *Corynebacterium diphtheriae* had been identified as the pathogen, the disease was named diphtheria. Even at an early stage physicians knew that an exotoxin had to be responsible, because the bacteria were always found only on the throat mucous and never in the damaged internal organs. Later this suspicion was proved beyond doubt by breeding the bacteria and isolating the poison, of which even a few millionths of a gramme are lethal.

Another toxin is associated with cholera. Asiatic cholera and all of its symptoms were described thousands of years ago in Indian Sanskrit writings (the Vedas, especially in the *Charakasamhita* and the *Susrutasamhita*) and called the great death. As trade expanded at the beginning of the 19th century, it spread from Asia to Europe, where it occurred frequently on an epidemic scale. It has still not been completely eradicated today. The spectrum of poisons deriving from microorganisms also includes those produced by various types of algae.

Highly potent poisons are produced by some types of microalgae, such as blue-green algae (Cyanophyceae), which occur mainly in fresh water. These are actually closer to bacteria than to the plant kingdom, and are therefore often classified as cyanobacteria. In the sea, dinoflagellates (Dinoflagellatae) are mainly responsible for the secondary toxicity of mussels.

For reasons which have yet to be explained, there sometimes occurs a massive increase (or bloom) in the number of dinoflagellates during the summer months from some ten to a hundred cells per ml sea water, to more than one hundred thousand; this results in a noticeable discolouration of the water known as red

Bacterial toxins are the pathogen for cholera, which was rife in Europe in the 19th century. International trade was one means by which it was transmitted. Cholera epidemic in Naples, 1884. Contemporary sketch by Eduardo Matania.

romuscular blockage, which leads to paralysis. Some algae occasionally multiply to a massive extent in fresh water, too, and in the past, this has resulted in widespread catastrophes, for which the blue-green algae in particular have been responsible. One extremely potent toxin has been isolated from the alga *Anabaena flos-aquae*, the neurotoxic alkaloid anatoxin A, which, in experiments, kills animals by respiratory paralysis within a few minutes. This was the alga responsible for the mass destruction of water birds and wild animals at Storm Lake, Iowa, in 1952. The blue-green alga *Microcystis aeruginosa* was studied by Paul Gorham and his colleagues. This alga killed thousands of cattle and sheep which came to drink from the reservoir of the Vaal Dam in Transvaal (South Africa).

Man, however, does not really suffer any serious ill-effects from algae (apart from dermatitis and conjunctivitis, which can occur in tropical and subtropical waters after contact with the blue-green alga *Lyngbya majuscula*; it can occur in northern latitudes, but has seldom been observed). One of the many fears of present times is that the military abuse of knowledge gained from current toxin research will lead to the development of new types of chemical weapon. Toxins described in this chapter could be produced synthetically, and would be capable of causing lethal mass poisoning with no less destructive potential than atomic weapons. A world-wide ban on all types of chemical weapon, including the synthetic toxins which are only partly covered by the biological arms convention, is therefore an urgent requirement of our times.

tide, which was described by Charles Darwin. One toxic species of the family Haptophyceae, the unicellular alga *Prymnesium parvum*, which occurs in brackish water as well as in the sea, was probably responsible for the blood-red discolouration of water mentioned in the Old Testament. The bloom of dinoflagellates off the coast of the Gulf of Mexico between 1971 and 1973 is estimated to have poisoned hundreds of tons of fish.

According to the centuries-old tradition of the Canadian coastal Indians, the occasional high toxicity of mussels is connected with the bloom of dinoflagellates. In the mid-1960s, biochemists isolated and described saxitoxin from *Gonyaulax catenella* and other dinoflagellates. Other toxins of this type were isolated from *Gonyaulax tamarensis*. All of these toxins work by neu-

Poisonous plants
(Toxic seeds, flowers and fruit)

One of man's earliest discoveries was that apart from their beauty and their considerable usefulness as a source of food and medicine, plants can also kill. Even in our seemingly highly advanced era of science and technology, they still retain the age-old fascination excited by their trinity of beauty, utility and death. The undeniable progress we have made in our knowledge of the biochemistry of plants can be contrasted today, and probably for many generations to come, with the almost unimaginable diversity of species, with different growth patterns and effects. Chemists and toxicologists throughout the ages have always felt challenged to understand, imitate and use plant ingredients, and this will doubtless remain the case in centuries to come.

For the layman, the number of plants which produce poison is just as impossible to grasp as the chemical structures and complex make-up of their biologically active constituents, to which the human organism can react in very different ways. The effects range from healing to sudden death, depending on the dose taken. There are plant poisons which act against microbes (antibiotics) or against insects (insecticides), or which provide a biological means of controlling a wide range of pests (pesticides). There are also plants which produce poison against other plants so as to be able to live, or even just survive, themselves.

The most important chemical parent substances found in plant poisons are alkaloids and glycosides.

Alkaloids, which were originally named for their alkali-like, i.e. basic behaviour, are a group of chemical compounds which usually have a complicated structure of nitrogenous closed rings—so-called nitrogen heterocycles. In plants, these alkaloids are usually bound to plant acids like salts.

Glycosides are compounds of one sugar, often glucose, and one non-saccharine component which is known as the aglycone. These aglycones, which are usually the actual active substances, are chemically very diverse. The most important glycosides are those which contain steroids as aglycones, and those which release prussic acid or mustard oil and related compounds by enzymatic processes. Saponins, which have steroids or triterpenes as aglycones, form a special group among the glycosidic plant substances; they are fairly widespread, and act by destroying the blood.

Apart from the alkaloids and glycosides, other important plant constituents are the toxic proteinaceous compounds (plant lectins) and various essential oils.

Most people today are largely ignorant about their native flora and fauna, and this frequently results in their being poisoned by plants.

Plant poisons feature even in the Old Testament (II Kings, 4, 39–40): "And one went out into the field ... and found a wild vine, and gathered thereof wild gourds his lap full, and came and shred them into the pot of pottage; for they knew them not. So they poured out for the men to eat. And it came to pass, as they were eating of the pottage, that they cried out, and said, 'O Thou man of God, there is death in the pot.' And they could not eat thereof."

As we have already mentioned, children are— and always have been—particularly at risk from poisonous plants. They are tempted by the often very attractively coloured berries and other plant parts to see what they taste like, especially the fruit of the cuckoo-pint (*Arum maculatum*), asparagus (*Asparagus officinalis*), holly (*Ilex aquifolium*), spindle tree (*Euonymus europaeus*), English yew (*Taxus baccata*) and guelder rose (*Viburnum opulus*). The leaves and flowers of the horse chestnut (*Aesculus hippocastanum*) contain the flavone glycoside quercitrin, while the bark and branches contain the coumarin glycoside aesculin (the aglycone is 6,7-dihydroxycoumarin). The active substance, however, must be the saponins, in which the seeds are particularly rich (eight to twenty-six percent). Symptoms of serious poisoning can occur in children after eating horse

Hemlock *(Conium maculatum)* contains the poisonous alkaloid coniine.
From: Hieronymus Bock, *Kreütterbuch*, Strasbourg, 1577.

frenzy, convulsions and, finally, death by respiratory paralysis. Pieces of root the size of a walnut are lethal for cows and horses, as is the foliage itself. Another plant which contains polyacetylene flourishes in southern Europe and in the British Isles, namely water dropwort *(Oenanthe crocata)*. This is regarded as one of the most dangerous poisonous plants found in these regions. Poisoning is known to have been caused by eating the thick tuberous roots of the plant (dead men's fingers), which taste like parsnips.

Many of the ornamental flowers and plants in our parks and gardens are also toxic, such as the primula *(Primula obconica)*, not to be confused with the oxlip *(Primula elatior)*, the cultivated varieties of the foxglove *(Digitalis sp.)* and the lily of the valley *(Convallaria majalis)*. Toxins can also be found in many other flowers, such as the paeony *(Paeonia officinalis)*, tulip *(Tulipa sp.)*, and narcissus *(Narcissus sp.)*. In the great tulip fields of Holland, allergic skin reactions are frequently observed; these are attributed to glycosidic tuliposides. Alarming articles appeared in leading medical journals at the turn of the century about the powerful skin irritant effect of the primula *(Primula obconica)*—indeed, it nearly came to a ban on the cultivation of the flower, different varieties of which were on the market. Primin (2-methoxy-6-pentyl-p-benzoquinone) was isolated as the active constituent responsible. Poison ivy *(Rhus toxicodendron)* also contains an allergen, urushiol (a mixture of catechols). This can cause extreme dermatitis on contact with the skin.

chestnuts; these take the form of anxiety and confusion, fever, stomach-ache and vomiting. But even the roots of plants are not always safely out of reach of children. The sweet-tasting root of the cowbane *(Cicuta virosa)*, which

$$HOCH_2-CH_2-CH_2-(C{\equiv}C)_2-(CH{=}CH)_3-\underset{\underset{OH}{|}}{C}H-CH_2-CH_2-CH_3$$

resembles celeriac, can cause serious poisoning. One of its constituents is highly poisonous cicutoxin, a polyacetylene compound, which can cause vomiting,

Some of the well-known members of the pea family (Fabaceae) also produce toxic alkaloids. The European yellow lupin *(Lupinus luteus)* and other varieties contain alkaloids in every part of the plant, with a particularly high concentration in the seeds. The common chemical structure of the lupin alkaloids is the quinolizidine ring, for instance in lupinin.

If large quantities of these bitter-tasting lupin species are mixed with animal feed, this can result in dangerous poisoning, and in particular in disorders of the heart and circulation.

More commonly known is the toxicity of the English yew *(Taxus baccata)* and of the yew family in general (Taxaceae), which decorate many parks and gardens, and which contain the alkaloid taxine, ephedrine and other constituents in all parts of the plant. The extract of fifty to one hundred needles can be lethal. One hour after taking the poison, symptoms such as vomiting, stomach-ache and colic occur, followed by an abnormal pulse rate, disorders of the liver and kidneys, and respiratory difficulties. After between one and a half and twenty-four hours, choking convulsions, a deep level of unconsciousness and death ensue. In ancient times, the yew was sacred to the gods of death. The Celts poisoned the tips of their lances and spears with yew extracts for use in hunting and battle; an early form of chemical weapon. At first sight, few people would connect the ivy-covered walls of an old house with poison, and yet the English ivy *(Hedera helix)* and others of the same family (Araliaceae) contain the triterpene saponins (aglycon, e.g. α-hederin) from hederasaponin in all parts of the plant, especially in the berries. It was mentioned as a drug by Dioscorides and Pliny—ivy too was an important cult plant in ancient times. Eating the berries initially causes excitement and convulsions, and the respiratory paralysis which follows can result in death. A fatal collapse can also follow a drop in blood pressure; children in particular have died in this way.

One shrub which can often be found in parks and gardens is the spindle tree *(Euonymus europaeus)* from the staff-tree family (Celastraceae). The fruit contains alkaloids (euonine) and cardiac glycosides which act in a similar way to digitalis. Fewer than forty of its fruit can be lethal. A particularly dangerous feature is that the first symptoms of poisoning do not appear until about fifteen hours after consumption. They take the form of irritation to the gastro-intestinal tract and bloody diarrhoea, as well as a high temperature, shortness of breath, circulatory disorders, convulsions, stupefaction and fainting.

The common red flowering paeony *(Paeonia officinalis)*, a member of the Paeoniaceae which is a garden flower which enjoys general popularity, contains the anthocyan glycosides paeonin and cyanine in its flowers, as well as tannin and probably also the alkaloid peregrinin in its seeds. The symptoms of poisoning are gastro-enteritis, vomiting and painful diarrhoea. The toxic effect has not been adequately explained.

The black locust *(Robinia pseudoacacia)*, which is also known as the false acacia, is often found in parks and forest plantations. It contains toxic proteinaceous substances (robin and phasin) in its bark, as well as robinin, which resembles an alkaloid, tannins and, as in most plants, essential oils. Taken orally (for example in sawdust), it can result in convulsions, hypersomnia and vomiting; in such cases children are particularly susceptible.

One plant which is of both botanical and toxicological interest is the giant hogweed *(Heracleum mantegazzianum)*. This umbellifer (Apiaceae), which can often grow to more than 3 metres high, was brought to Europe from the Caucasus in 1890, and is found as an ornamental plant in many botanical and private gardens nowadays. There are reports of wild plants in Mexico. If the stem is cut or broken and sap comes into contact with the skin, considerable local inflammation occurs in the presence of sunlight (known as photodermatitis). The active substances are derivatives of coumarin with a fused furan ring.

Irresponsible behaviour is not infrequently the cause of plant poisoning. On one occasion, for example, an adult collected a cup-ful of apple pips, swallowed them all at once, and died. Like a wide range of other seeds— e.g. those of plums, cherries, apricots, peaches, bitter almonds, lemons, pears and elderberries—apple pips contain so-called cyanogenetic (or cyanophoric) glycosides. In 1803 the Berlin physician Johann Schrader discovered that chopped bitter almonds release prussic acid. Chopping destroys the cells, and the cyanophoric glycosides come into contact with an enzyme (β-glucosidase) which is also present in the almond. It breaks them down in a binary toxic reaction. This releases α-hydroxy nitriles as aglycones (sugar-free residue), which are then broken down by the slightly acidic cell sap or enzymes (nitrilases) into carbonyl components and prussic acid. The best-known cyanophoric glycoside, that of the bitter almond, was isolated by Pierre Jean Robiquet and Antoine-François Boutron-Chalard in 1830, and called amygdalin. Bitter almond poisoning, especially of children, is not uncommon even today. The toxicity of these plant seeds was abused in ancient Egypt, while the Greek physician Dioscorides described their effect back in the first century A.D.

Since enzymes in the human body can combat prussic acid to a certain extent, no harmful effects will be observed if a very small dose of a few milligrammes is taken; the amount varies greatly from individual to individual.

Depending on the environment, some glycosides can cause poisoning in developing countries in the tropics, where the people sometimes have a very unbalanced diet: examples are bamboo shoots *(Bambusa vulgaris)*, cassava *(Manihot esculenta)*, the yam *(Dioscorea sp.)*, the sweet potato or batata *(Ipomoea batatas)*, the Sieva bean *(Phaseolus lunatus)* and sugar cane *(Saccharum officinarum)*. These can cause not only acute poisoning.

Some nervous diseases, cretinism and endemic goitre have been linked to the chronic consumption of prussic acid.

As has already been mentioned, confusion and ignorance of the danger of plants results in emergency treatment for poisoning being required time and time again. The specialist literature is full of such cases. An example which is often quoted in historical texts is that of the hemlock *(Conium maculatum)*, which was used, according to Plato's account, to execute Socrates in 399 B.C. This plant has been confused with parsley and celeriac, its fruit with aniseed and fennel, and its roots with horse-radish. The main toxin is a plant alkaloid, the piperidine derivative coniine, with its characteristic smell, even when well diluted, of mouse urine—it was also, incidentally, the first alkaloid to be produced synthetically; this was achieved by Albert Ladenburg in 1886. Its effects range from excitement and depression to motorial disturbance and death by respiratory paralysis.

The most poisonous plant in Central Europe is thought to be the wolfsbane *(Aconitum napellus)*, a member of the buttercup family (Ranunculaceae), which also contains several alkaloids. The main alkaloid, aconitine, is one of the most potent vegetable poisons, and was used, along with *Conium maculatum*, in ancient and mediaeval times in medicine, but also as a murder weapon. The Indians and Greeks used it as an arrow poison. After only a few minutes, the mouth begins to burn, and the victim experiences a cold sweat. Nausea, vomiting and diarrhoea, and an unbearable feeling of coldness, then set in. The limbs are paralyzed and breathing slows down; death can occur after only twenty minutes. The lethal dose of pure aconitine for an adult is about 1 to 2 mg; confusing it with parsley may occur.

Immediately after the two World Wars, parts of plants, especially leaves, were often eaten by the hungry people of Europe as "wild vegetables". Many people suffered as a consequence, when they accidentally included poisonous plants, such as the leaves of the deadly nightshade, in their meals.

One ornamental shrub which is found mainly in parks is the laburnum or golden rain *(Laburnum anagyroides)*, a member of the pea family (Fabaceae), all parts of which contain the highly toxic alkaloid cytisine as well as the amino alcohol choline. This alkaloid has a similar effect to nicotine, and is a constituent of the Bulgarian smokers' cure Tabex. The seeds of this shrub resemble beans. Even two seeds can seriously affect a small child. The roots of the black henbane *(Hyoscyamus niger)* resemble black salsify *(Scorzonera hispanica)*. The white hellebore *(Veratrum album)*, a member of the lily family, is common in high mountain areas. The poisons it contains are, among others, the steroid alkaloids protoveratrine A and B and germerine, jervan and cevan alkaloids as well as chelidonic acid and veratric acid, and phenoles. Its roots have been confused with those of the gentian, which are used to distil a spirit. This causes powerful convulsions followed by death.

The leaves of the poisonous meadow saffron *(Colchicum autumnale)*, another member of the lily family, contain the toxic alkaloid colchicine. They have in the past been confused with the wild garlic *(Allium ursinum)*, although this too should be avoided, because the vinyl disulphide which is the main constituent of its essential oils can cause severe gastro-enteritis, an inflammatory disease of the gastro-intestinal area. The symptoms of colchicine poisoning are vomiting, bloody diarrhoea, loss of consciousness and paralysis, and finally respiratory failure. Just five seeds of the meadow saffron can be lethal under certain circumstances.

Even the seeds of the European red beech *(Fagus silvatica)*, the famous beechnuts, are considered dangerous, because thirty to fifty of these can cause vomiting, diarrhoea, convulsions, paralysis and loss of consciousness. Researchers are not yet completely certain about the active principle responsible for poisoning, as it contains several constituents, such as fagin, substances which destroy vitamin B, phenolic acid and small amounts of saponins, alkaloids and tannins. Even the world-famous cookbook *Larousse Gastronomique* is not infallible: it claimed that rhubarb leaves could be eaten "like spinach". Many cases of poisoning have been caused by the oxalic acid they contain, especially in post-war periods and other times of deprivation, resulting in disorders of the calcium metabolism. Apart from vomiting, diarrhoea and circulatory collapse, this can

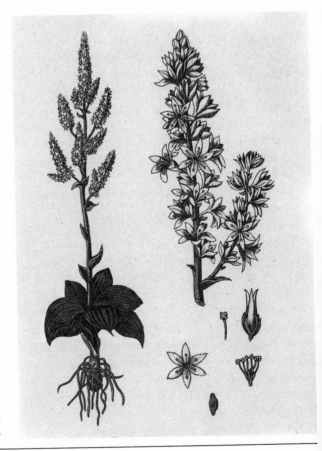

» 82 «

Even just a few seeds of the meadow saffron *(Colchicum autumnale)* can be deadly; they contain the alkaloid colchicine. Recent research has shown that this poison can inhibit cell division, and can therefore be used to control malignant tumours. Copperplate from: Johann Samuel Halle, *Die Deutschen Giftpflanzen*, Berlin, 1784.

lead to serious liver and kidney damage and anuria. These phenomena can probably be traced back to anthraquinone glycosides. In spring, the leaves contain 0.5 to 1 percent total anthraquinones, for the most part in the reduced form of anthrahydroquinones, which severely irritate the tissues. Strong suspicions have also been aroused recently that anthraquinones act mutagenically, i.e., that they cause hereditary defects.

An unbalanced diet can also endanger health, as has already been stated in connection with cyanophoric glycosides. For example, some varieties of cabbage contain mustard oils and glycosides which release related compounds (glucosinolates); these can inhibit the production of the thyroid hormone thyroxine.

The process of hydrolitic or enzymatic release of isothiocyanates by plants is familiar to us in our everyday lives, even if the layman does not particularly recognize or even notice it, for example, when cress is chopped or horseradish is grated, or when one bites a caper or radish, or when one notices the smell of cabbage leaves rotting in a rubbish bin. One example often quoted in toxicological literature is that of black mustard *(Brassica nigra)*, a member of the crucifer family (Cruciferae), whose seeds in particular contain up to 4.5 percent sinigrin. This produces up to one percent allyl isothiocyanate by hydrolysis. Chemists generally refer to this compound as mustard oil.

The acute reaction to skin contact takes the form of severe local irritation. If the victim is exposed for a relatively long period, the mustard oil can penetrate the skin and cause serious inflammation. Relatively large doses taken orally cause severe irritation to the gastrointestinal tract—after absorption, excitement, convulsions, paralysis, collapse and death ensue.

Hydroxy-3-butenyl-isothiocyanate is produced by a rape-seed glucosinolate (progoitrin) by (enzymatic) break-down, and this quickly cyclizes to vinyl oxazolidenethione. This in turn prevents the oxidation of iodide to iodine in the organism, so that the thyrosin produced by the body can no longer be iodized, with the result that there is an insufficient supply of the thyroid hormone thyroxine. This affects a large number of metabolic processes linked with such serious symptoms as stunted growth, mental retardation and goitre. Recently the oxazolidenethiones produced by various mustard oils have also been suspected of having a mutagenic or carcinogenic effect. This does not of course mean that no radishes, cabbage or mustard should be eaten, but rather that a balanced diet should be observed. Sometimes the substances which cause concern can be destroyed by the method of preparation used: for example, deep-frozen Brussels sprouts release only 1/100 of the quantity of allyl mustard oil released by the fresh vegetable, but this detracts from their taste, because it is these very break-down products which make sprouts so delicious. A number of toxic vegetable foodstuffs lose their harmful effects only after being cooked. Eating raw beans, for instance, can cause vomiting, diarrhoea and a high temperature. Only after heating are the toxic proteinaceous substances broken-down and destroyed.

Even some extremely common foodstuffs contain alkaloids, for example the green parts and sprouts of the potato *(Solanum tuberosum)*. The active principle is the alkaloid glycoside solanine. The sugar-free residue solanidine, an alkaloid with a steroid skeleton, is produced by hydrolysis. Solanine is also present in other members of the nightshade family, mainly in the unripe berries and green shoots. Irritation of the digestive organs, diarrhoea, haemolytic symptoms and skin disorders such as eczema are all indications of solanine poisoning. These are followed by neurological symptoms with paralysis and convulsions, culminating in death from respiratory failure.

A toxic steroid alkaloid glycoside (tomatine) can be found in the leaves of the wild tomato and in green tomatoes *(Lycopersicon esculentum)*.

In Africa and North and South America, poisonous plants sometimes inflict great damage on livestock. More than one hundred thousand cattle die in South America every year from eating such plants.

A number of poisons from the plant kingdom have been used in the past by quack doctors as abortifacients, for example the oil of the creeping juniper, also known as the savin *(Juniperus sabina)*, with constituents such as sabinol, sabinene, thujol and other terpene derivatives.

Such applications usually had fatal consequences, because the intended effect was only realized when extremely high doses were administered. The oil seriously damages the kidneys, liver and womb. Death often occurred in a state of central paralysis and deep unconsciousness. Today, savin preparations are still used occasionally in veterinary medicine. The apiol contained in parsley oil was also used in abortions, and also caused serious poisoning.

The use of poisons to terminate pregnancy has always presented a great risk to health and life, something

that we in the "age of the pill" can scarcely envisage. In most countries, the use of such preparations has always been punishable. In ancient Rome, the penalty for administering love potions and abortifacients was hard labour in the mines, or banishment in the case of the upper classes; if the patient died, the quack doctor faced the death penalty.

The French midwife Catherine Voisin won notoriety in about 1680. She did a roaring trade in poisons and love potions, with the courtiers of the Sun King among her best customers. She also performed some two thousand five hundred abortions, which not infrequently ended in death. According to her own admission, she used mixtures mainly of henbane, thornapple and Spanish fly. In those days, and in the centuries which followed, a huge army of charlatans like her could be found both in Court circles and among the common people.

Any reader of detective stories will be familiar with the use of vegetable poisons in murders and suicides, such as in the case, of which a film was later made, of Dr. Crippen, who murdered his wife in 1910 with scopolamine, an alkaloid poison which is found in various members of the nightshade family (cf. narcotics).

As has already been mentioned in the preceding chapters, these criminal cases are of interest to the toxicologist inasmuch as solving them often went hand in hand with major advances in the analysis of poisons. In 1864 a certain Dr. de la Pommerais stood trial in France for a murder in which he had used the digitalis glycosides of the foxglove (Digitalis purpurea). Forensic chemists initially suspected the use of alkaloids, but could not find evidence of these; only after intensive work did they succeed in finding traces of digitalis in the victim's vomit, by using a preparation made from a frog's heart: at that time, digitalis was an uncommon murder weapon. Another example was as follows: in 1978 London newspapers carried reports of a murder

LE PORTRAIT DE LA VOISIN.

by means of ricin, a highly-toxic proteinaceous substance obtained from the seeds of the castor bean (Ricinus communis). As the victim was waiting at a bus-stop, a tiny, hollow metal ball the size of a pin-head, containing 3 µl of the poison, was stabbed into his leg. The minuteness of the dose demonstrates the extreme toxicity of the poison. A number of plants, especially legumes and a few euphorbias, contain toxic proteins of this type, which are often described as toxalbumins or phytohaemagglutinins. It is more accurate to speak of plant lectins, which are proteins which can bind specifically to carbohydrates. The most notable examples are the afore-mentioned ricin from the seeds of the castor bean, and abrine, from the rosary pea *(Abrus precatorius)*. Red blood corpuscles in a suspension coagulate if even a very weak ricin solution is added. The castor bean belongs to the spurge family (Euphorbiaceae). Apart from ricin, its seeds contain ricinine, an alkaloid of the pyridine series. The fruit of the castor bean causes sickness and diarrhoea, convulsions and tachycardia, and as few as twenty seeds are considered absolutely lethal. Castor oil, which is used as a laxative, should not be equated with the poisonous parts of the plant. It is obtained by crushing the seeds, whereby the toxic constituents are left behind in the cake. The main constituent of castor oil is the triglyceride of ricinoleic acid (12-hydroxy-oleic acid). Ricin can be denatured by cooking. It was the first plant lectin to be produced by Rudolf Kobert and H. Stillmark with a yield of three percent in 1888. In 1891, Paul Ehrlich discovered that mice could be made immune to ricin by giving them repeated injections of non-lethal doses. He also succeeded in immunizing mice with the serum of other mice which had been treated with ricin. This led him to postulate detoxification by antibodies in the organism. The wider concept of the antigen was later coined for ricin. We also encounter the antigen in various peptide poisons from the animal kingdom.

Vegetable poisons were used by different peoples in different ways to make their weapons more effective, but there is room here for only a glimpse of this subject. A number of plant toxins have been used to poison arrows and blowpipe darts, for example strychnine, which is derived from species of *Strychnos* and is sometimes used in Malaya. Strychnine demands a short description, because it is one of the particularly striking poisons. The seeds of the nux vomica poison nut *(Strychnos nux-vomica)*, of the logania family (Loganiaceae), contain between two and five percent alkaloids. The nux vomica is found from East India to Australia. The main constituent is strychnine, which accounts for about half of the alkaloid content; the remainder consists of brucine and other companion alkaloids. Strychnine poisoning causes restlessness, anxiety, vomiting and sudden tetanic spasms and respirato-

ry arrest. These symptoms take the form of fits, and if continued will rapidly result in death. The victim remains fully conscious during these painful attacks.

The nux vomica was described by Valerius Cordus as early as 1540. The alkaloid was isolated in 1818 by the Frenchman Joseph-Bienaimé Caventou and Pierre Joseph Pelletier.

Strychnine nitrate, which dissolves readily in water, is occasionally used in medicine to counteract symptoms of paralysis, and was also used in earlier times against circulatory disorders and debility. In Southeast Asia, strychnos seeds are chewed, supposedly to guard against cholera and snake bites. Strychnine is still used in some places today to treat wheat for rodent control, so-called poisoned wheat.

Let us now turn to another kind of hunting poison, namely curare. The Spanish conquerors of South America made the acquaintance of curare-tipped arrows at the cost of their lives, and they were known in Europe as early as the 16th century. Many naturalists tried to discover the secret recipes used by the different tribes of American natives. Alexander von Humboldt was the first to achieve this. The Indians use water to extract the deadly arrow poison from the bark of *Strychnos toxifera*, a liana indigenous to the Orinoco River, and other species of strychnos. It contains numerous indole alkaloids, most of which have the chemical character of quaternary ammonium salts. A few are tertiary bases and the active principles of the South American calabash curare—the calabash is the gourd in which the poison is kept. One of its most effective alkaloids is C-toxiferine I, which is five to ten times as poisonous as aconitine. This must be distinguished from tube curare, whose active constituents are the biquaternary bis-isoquinolines, contained in species of *Chondrodendron*. Tube curare and curare are sometimes used as adjuvants in anaesthesia to help relax the muscles. Even extremely small doses of curare can block the acetylcholine receptors, thereby paralyzing the organs at the end of the motorial nerves of the striated voluntary muscles (i.e. not the heart muscle), resulting in complete paralysis and suffocation, as the chest movements cease. The most horrific characteristic for the victim is that he experiences the advancing muscular paralysis while fully conscious. Curare is only absorbed by the gastro-intestinal tract in very large doses, so the flesh of poisoned animals can be eaten without risk.

Strophanthins, which are widely known because of their use in medicine (they are extremely cardioactive glycosides), belong to another group of poisons. They are found in the seeds of South African species of *Strophanthus*, such as *Strophanthus gratus* and *Strophanthus kombé*, and are used as arrow poisons in Africa and on the Malay archipelago. Even elephants can be killed with extracts of *Strophanthus gratus*.

Species of *Strophanthus* were first brought from Africa to Europe by the famous Scottish explorer David Livingstone in 1843. Strophanthin poisoning causes vomiting, diarrhoea, fluctuations in blood pressure and fibrillation of the ventricles of the heart, leading to heart failure. The aglycone in strophanthin, strophanthidin, is very similar in structure to the aglycones of digitalis glycosides. g-Strophanthin is identical to ouabain, obtained from species of *Acokanthera* (Apocynaceae).

Vegetable poisons have also been used in other ways for hunting or pest control, and still are today. For example, in East Africa the natives pour extracts of *Tephrosia vogeli* into the water to drug fish, which are then collected. After being placed in fresh water for a while, the fish regain consciousness, and can be kept alive until needed.

On the Malay archipelago, the roots of the *Derris elliptica*, which contain rotenones, are used as a fish poison, and to tip arrows. The natives chew the roots, then dive near a shoal of fish, where they spit out the pulp. They then surface, wash out their mouths, and dive again to gather their stunned prey.

During early attempts at pest control, vegetable poisons were used in a number of very diverse preparations. In his *Kreütterbuch* (Herbal) of 1577, Hieronymus Bock mentions twelve plant substances for eradicating lice, mites and nits, eleven for fleas, and thirty-seven for flies and gnats. He gave a vivid account of how insects are poisoned by eating or coming into contact with the white hellebore *(Veratrum album)* boiled in milk: "... boiled in milk and set before the flies ... all that eat thereof must swell up and burst ...".

As early as 1690, nicotine wash was used to control greenfly, and in 1746 it was applied to plum beetles. In the 20th century, nicotine preparations were produced industrially, and were used until the introduction of new synthetic insecticides (although 100 tons of them were still being used in German vineyards in 1934).

As much as a hundred years ago people used what were known as "Dalmatian" or "Persian" insect powders, whose principal ingredient was the dried and crushed flowers of *Chrysanthemum cinnerariaefolium*. Pyrethrins, the active constituents, are still used today for pest control, although they are now produced synthetically.

Many specimens of Fabaceae contain rotenones, and many species of *Chrysanthemum* pyrethrins (e.g. pyrethrin I) which are again playing an increasingly impor-

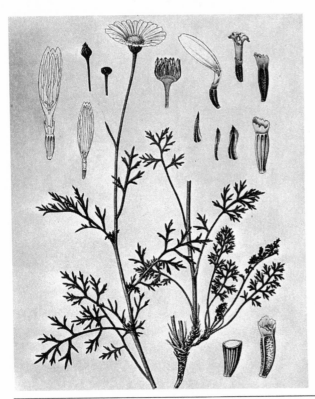

tant role in pest control today, and can now be produced synthetically. Their effects were already known more than a hundred years ago, and they were used either als "Dalmatian" or "Persian" insect powders, depending on origin, which contained the dried and ground flowers of *Chrysanthemum cinnerariaefolium*.

The extremely colourful history of the use and abuse of vegetable poisons ranges over other areas, too, which often strike us as antediluvian today, but which were perfectly commonplace a few centuries ago and, indeed, are still current among a few tribes in Africa and South America. One example is provided by the *Gelsemium* plants of the family Loganiaceae: these are indigenous to America, and the numerous alkaloids in their rootstock were used by the Indians for ordeals, to prove the guilt or innocence of a suspect. The suspect's guilt was proven if he died, and his innocence if he survived by vomiting up the plant extract. In Central and West Africa the calabar (or ordeal) bean *(Physostigma venenosum)*, which contains the indole alkaloid physostigmine, was used for the same purpose. It is interesting to

note that the alkaloid of the calabar bean can completely cure the muscular paralysis brought on by South American curare—in other words, one poison acts as an antidote to another. Another poison used in Africa comprises the cardioactive alkaloid mixtures contained in *Erythrophleum suaveolens*, earlier known as *Erythrophleum guineense*. Ordeals were particularly common in West Africa. The Balante tribe alone is reported by explorers to have lost some three thousand five hundred of its people in this way in 1911 and 1912. As is always the case wherever such customs occur, this one also had its own particular features. For example, if the suspect was a chieftain, the poison could be given to a proxy or to an animal. Anyone with connections in "high places" or who was not without means, would arrange for an emetic to be mixed into the drink.

Mathieu Joseph Bonaventure Orfila, the pioneer of toxicology. Contemporary lithograph by François Séraphin Delpech. Deutsche Staatsbibliothek, Berlin.

Jean-Servais Stas was the first man to succeed in detecting alkaloids in human organism.
Contemporary representation.

The death cap (Amanita phalloides) is the most poisonous toadstool found in Central Europe.

The false morel or lorchel (Gyromitra esculenta) was eaten and enjoyed for many years, but it often caused fatal poisoning. It was not until 1967 that the nitrogenous toxin which it contains, and which acts in a similar way to the toxins of the Amanitae, was identified.

The ink cap (Coprinus atramentarius) is a curiosity among fungi. It causes a marked hypersensitivity to alcohol.

The fly agaric (Amanita muscaria) is generally only eaten in error in Italy, where it may be confused with the edible golden agaric (Amanita caesarea), to which it bears a superficial resemblance. Because of its intoxicating properties, the fly agaric was honoured as a deity in ancient India.

Disinfection brigade during the Hamburg cholera epidemic, 1892.

Spore heads of mould fungus (Aspergillus flavus), which produce highly carcinogenic aflatoxins.

Ergot (Claviceps purpurea), which used to be responsible for poisoning on an epidemic scale, especially in France and Germany, flourishes particularly well on ears of rye.

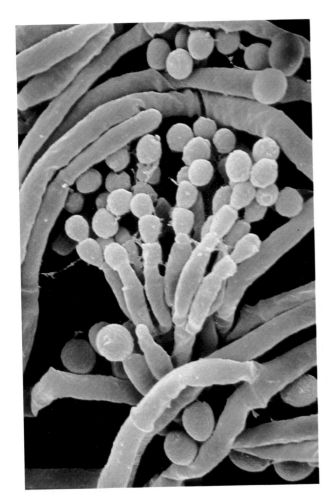

The sweet-tasting, celeriac-like root of the cowbane *(Cicuta virosa)* has sometimes been confused with that of edible plants, resulting in poisoning.

Socrates taking the cup of hemlock.
Jacques Louis David, *The death of Socrates*, 1787.
Metropolitan Museum of Art, New York.

The most poisonous plant in Central Europe is the wolfsbane *(Aconitum napellus)*. It contains the alkaloid aconitine, which was not infrequently used as a murder poison in ancient and mediaeval times.

Multifoliate lupins *(Lupinus polyphyllus)* and other bitter-tasting lupins can poison farm animals if they are mixed into their feed.

Preceding page:
Some Indian tribes tipped their blowpipe darts with curare; a Yaguá from the
upper reaches of the Amazon.

A Jivaro Indian (from Ecuador) with the arrow poison curare.

The strychnine contained in the nux vomica *(Strychnos nux vomica)* was used in Malaysia as an arrow poison. Today it is still used occasionally in medicine as a cure for paralysis.

The oleander *(Nerium oleander)* contains the effective cardioglycoside oleandrin.

Cardioactive digitalis glycosides from the foxglove *(Digitalis purpurea)* are among the most important raw materials used in the production of pharmaceuticals today.

The wood of the arbor vitae (*Thuja* sp.) contains α-thujaplicin, which has an antimicrobial effect, and thus offers protection against fungi.
Alabaster relief from the palace of Ashurnasirpal II in Calah, 9th century B.C.
Vorderasiatisches Museum, Staatliche Museen zu Berlin.

The use of plants as abortifacients in ancient and mediaeval times cost many lives. These were obtained from itinerant pedlars.
Figure of a so-called *Troger* (drug-seller), 17th century. Wood and ivory. Medizinhistorisches Institut der Universität Zürich.

An African member of the spurge family, *Croton tiglium*, contains the irritant known as croton oil. It has been established that this has a pronounced co-carcinogenic effect.

In the first millennium A.D., such ordeals were also quite prevalent in Europe. They were not banned by the Church until 1215.

Other peoples used animal and vegetable poisons not only to try a suspect, but also for executions pure and simple. The most famous example is the poisoning of Socrates with hemlock in 399 B.C. In ancient Egypt the prussic acid glycosides contained in peach stones were used instead of hemlock. Even today, criminals are executed in some States in the USA by poisoning (with cyanide, for instance). Species of *Lithospermum*, which contain nitrile glycosides, have been used for a completely different purpose. North American Indian tribes used them as a contraceptive, similar to the drug kwao keur which is used in Asia—especially Thailand. This is extracted from the root-tubers of *Pueraria mirifica*, a type of leguminous plant. But many of the deadly plant poisons which have been listed here have served man for medicinal purposes, or even been life savers, as the following small selection of examples will illustrate.

The dictum in Hegel's dialectics that everything bears its own antithesis within itself was anticipated, at least as far as poison is concerned, by the great physician Paracelsus, when he said: "All things are poison/and nothing without poison/Only the dose makes a thing not a poison." Until Paracelsus's time, this fact, which had been common knowledge in ancient Greece, had long been forgotten: there was only one term for poison and medication in ancient Greece, and that was *pharmacon*. The peoples of classical Antiquity were perfectly aware of the relationship between therapeutical and toxic doses. This was established by carrying out experiments on prisoners of war, slaves and prisoners facing the death penalty. Thus in days gone by, aqueous extracts of bitter almonds (prussic acid) were widely used to cure convulsive coughing, asthma and colic. The dangerous coniine contained in the hemlock *(Conium maculatum)* proved efficacious against asthma, angina pectoris and severe pains,

such as those suffered by cancer victims. Cicutoxin, from the cowbane *(Cicuta virosa)*, helped to relieve epilepsy, aconitine from the wolfsbane *(Aconitum napellus)* helped to counteract severe neuralgia and chronic inflammation of the joints, and colchicine from the meadow saffron *(Colchicum autumnale)* was used to relieve gout. The bark of subtropical trees of the genera *Cinchona*, such as the South American cinchona *Cinchona* sp. (Rubiaceae), contains some thirty alkaloids, the most important of which, cinchonine and quinine, were discovered by Joseph-Bienaimé Caventou and Pierre Joseph Pelletier in 1820. The term *Cinchona* was chosen by Linnaeus in

1742, after a Peruvian viceroy who, as legend would have it, recovered from a fever in 1638 after taking cinchona bark. Cinchona has been used in Europe since

the 17th century as an antipyretic and as a remedy against malaria, because it rapidly destroys malaria plasmodia. This alkaloid has definite healing properties, although in this case, too, relatively high doses can produce symptoms of poisoning, such as dizziness, headaches and temporary blindness.

Apart from numerous other alkaloids, *Rauwolfia serpentina* and other species of *Rauwolfia* found in the tropics and subtropics contain the indole alkaloid reserpine, especially in the roots. It was not until 1952 that Emil Schlittler succeeded in isolating it and explaining its structure.

Shortly thereafter it was used in medicine as a means of reducing the blood pressure and as a tranquillizer, as were the alkaloid extracts as a whole. In India, the raw extract or ground roots have for many years been administered to combat fever, snake bites and high blood pressure. *Rauwolfia* was named after the Augsburg physician and botanist Leonhard Rauwolf, who travelled to the Middle East at the end of the 16th century in order to study in more detail the medicinal plants to be found there (although he never set eyes on India or on *Rauwolfia serpentina* himself). The basic ring structure of reserpine is that of the β-carboline, which is also found in yohimbine, the alkaloid of the West African yohimbé tree *(Pausinystalia yohimba)* of the madder family (Rubiaceae). Yohimbine was discovered by Leopold Julius Spiegel in 1896. Because it dilates the blood vessels, it has been used to counteract circulatory disturbances and to reduce the blood pressure, as well as to increase the sex drive, principally of animals, but also of humans.

It has recently been discovered that colchicine inhibits cell division, so it is now used in certain cases to treat various cancers. The alkaloids of the tropical periwinkle *(Catharanthus roseus)* are used in the treatment of certain forms of leukemia. Silymarin, which is found in the seeds of the milk thistle *(Silybum marianum)*, not only counteracts two powerful liver toxins, phalloidin and amanitine, which are responsible for death cap poisoning (early stage), but has also become a very valuable medicine for the liver and gallbladder in general.

The common foxglove and the Grecian foxglove *(Digitalis purpurea* and *Digitalis lanata)* of the family Scrophulariaceae must be among the best-known poisonous and medicinal plants in Central Europe. They grow in the wild, but are also cultivated, and all parts of the plants contain highly toxic cardioactive digitalis glycosides (see p. 85), as well as steroid saponins and tannins. The German specialist in internal medicine, Bernhard Naunyn, once said that he could not envisage being a doctor without digitalis.

Digitalis purpurea and *Digitalis lanata* have been studied more closely than almost any other plant species, yet we are still discovering more and more about them. Over seventy cardioactive glycosides from various species of *Digitalis* have now been isolated and described. Foxgloves have been used in popular medicine for centuries. English manuscripts from the 10th century—some of whose contents date back to the 6th century—tell of the use of *Digitalis* as an external medicine.

In his famous herbal *De historia stirpium ...*, which appeared in Germany in 1543, Leonhard Fuchs called the plant, which he had described and illustrated, *Digitalis*, a name which was then adopted by Linnaeus in his bo-

A N

A C C O U N T

OF THE

F O X G L O V E,

A N D

Some of its Medical Ufes :

W I T H

PRACTICAL REMARKS ON DROPSY,

AND OTHER DISEASES.

B Y

WILLIAM WITHERING, M. D.

Phyfician to the General Hofpital at Birmingham.

—— *nonumque prematur in annum.*

HORACE.

BIRMINGHAM: PRINTED BY M. SWINNEY;
F O R
G. G. J. AND J. ROBINSON, PATERNOSTER-ROW, LONDON.

M, DCC, LXXXV.

tanical taxonomy in 1753. Modern digitalis research began with the physician William Withering from Birmingham, whose work, published in 1785, provided the stimulus for the use of digitalis in therapy. But it was not until 1867 that one of the most important active substances, digitoxin, was isolated in an almost pure form (ninety to ninety-five percent) by the French apothecary Claude-Adolph Nativelle, after the Académie de Médecine de France had established the Orfila Prize in 1864 to stimulate research in this field. As early as 1844, the Société de Pharmacie had put up a prize for research into the constituents of digitalis. This was won by the Parisian doctor Augustin-Eugène Homolle for his discovery of "digitalin" (which we now know to be a mixture of digitoxin, gitoxin and a few companion glycosides), although he did not find a solution to the problem of dosage, the composition fluctuating considerably depending on location and processing.

Chemically pure cardiac glycosides were produced only after 1930, and in some cases not until after 1950. According to research by Arthur Stoll, the crystalline glycosides isolated from *Digitalis purpurea*, digitoxin and gitoxin, are not primary constituents of the plant, but are products of the partial saponification of the original constituents (foxglove glycosides A and B). These glycosides are broken-down by enzymes into digitoxin and glucose or gitoxin and glucose. Hydrolysis in an acid solution produces the aglycones digitoxigenin and gitoxigenin and the deoxy sugar digitoxose and glucose. *Digitalis lanata* contains an additional glycoside which, when treated with enzymes, produces digoxin—or digoxigenin if treated with acid. The related aglycones (genins) are, chemically speaking, lactones, with a carbon skeleton corresponding to that of the sterols. The first signs of poisoning are a considerable slowing-down of cardiac activity (bradycardia). Subsequently the victim will experience dicrotism, nausea and vomiting. If a lethal dose is taken, the blood pressure rises dramatically, the pulse rate drops and death results from cardiac arrest.

The oleander *(Nerium oleander)*, a member of the dogbane family (Apocynaceae), can be found in parks and gardens at European latitudes. All parts of the plant contain effective cardiac glycosides. The oleander is said to be used still today by people in the Mediterranean area who wish to poison themselves in order, for instance, to be exempted from military service.

Lily of the valley *(Convallaria majalis)*, a liliaceous plant (Liliaceae), also contains cardioactive digitalis glycosides, the most important being convallatoxin, as well as saponins and an essential oil with a characteristic smell.

Finally, we should mention the Christmas rose *(Helleborus niger)* of the buttercup family (Ranunculaceae), which produces cardiac glycosides in the form of hellebrin, large amounts of which are present in the roots in particular. It also contains saponins (helleborin) and essential oils.

To sum up, it is true to say that we can scarcely imagine medicine without cardiac glycosides. The constituents of toad poisons (see p.114) are closely related to all of these cardioactive substances (i.e. the aglycones).

One thing of which pharmacologists and toxicologists can be in no doubt in the 20th century is that many plants have antibiotic properties. They produce substances which prevent bacteria, fungi and protozoa from living and growing. Their healing properties are of most interest to man, but we should like here to mention some substances. In the Ebers papyri and in the clay tablets in the world-famous library of Nineveh, the onion is described as a means of treating septic wounds. In his book *De medicina*, Celsus, who worked under the Roman emperor Tiberius, listed a number of plants with which suppurating wounds could be treated. The chemical composition of these plants is very diverse: they range from constituents of essential oils, such as the thymol present in thyme *(Thymus serpyllum)*, from which it acquires its characteristic smell (it was used as an antiseptic as early as 1887), and plant constituents which release mustard oils, e.g. p-hydroxybenzyl isothiocyanate from mustard *(Sinapis alba)* and other unsaturated organosulphurous compounds (e.g. in crushed garlic), to unsaturated lactones (e.g. anemonin in the pasque-flower *Anemone pulsatilla*), as well as a wide range of glycosides, quinones, coumarins, acetylenes, alkaloids and many other substances.

Timber too contains antimicrobial poisons which protect it mainly against fungi. One such heartwood toxin is the glycosidically bound taxicatigenin of the English yew *(Taxus baccata)*, which is a 3,5-dimethoxy phenol, or the α-thujaplicin found in species of arbor vitae. A wide range of phenolic bodies in herbs (caraway, fennel, coriander and aniseed) can kill bacteria and fungi, such as flavonol glycosides and hydroxybenzoic acid as glycosides or esters.

Apart from "producing" poisons, certain plants can also have a "secondary" toxic effect, i.e. they absorb harmful substances from the soil. For example, some plants flourish particularly well on the slag heaps of ore mines, causing toxic heavy metals to accumulate. The calamine violet *(Viola calaminaria)*, which is found in Belgium, the Netherlands and in the Federal Republic of Germany (in the Rhineland and Westphalia) is a well-known "zinc plant". Nothing is yet known about the danger to man of such plants because their very place of origin makes them unsuitable for use in pharmacology. Another example is provided by species of *Astragalus*, which flourish in selenium-rich soils, and incorporate selenium as opposed to sulphur in important metabolites (e.g. as selenoamino acids).

In the fluorine-containing soils of Africa, South America and Australia, members of the genus *Acacia* can incorporate extremely toxic fluoroacetic acid—used as a sabotage poison by the military—as well as more poisonous or non-toxic fluorine-substituted fatty acids.

Many plants can accumulate nitrates in their stalks and leaves, especially if they are well fertilized. This includes certain types of vegetable, such as soya beans, cucumbers, beet, radishes, spinach and mangel-wurzel. For adults, this is not usually dangerous (although we should not ignore the possibility that nitrosamine, which is an important carcinogen, might build up in the organism), but infants who are fed large quantities of spinach—with an excessive nitrate-content—can suffer serious poisoning. Even the improper storage of vegetables can cause some of the nitrate to be reduced to nitrite. This reduction also takes place in the mouth and in the upper small intestine of infants, as a result of the bacteria which are present there. The nitrite is absorbed in the bloodstream and causes oxidation of the blood pigment haemoglobin to haemiglobin. This inhibits the respiratory function (oxygen transport) of the erythrocytes. Infants still have relatively large quantities of foetal haemoglobin, which is oxidized by nitrite twice as quickly as in adults, whose enzyme system reduces the haemiglobin back to haemoglobin. This metabolic process is not fully developed in infants.

But adults too are at risk, although in a biochemically different way. If they consume large quantities of food containing nitrates or nitrites, as well as foodstuffs containing amines, such as various types of vegetable, fish, cheese, wine or medicaments, there is a possibility, in the acid environment of the stomach, of a chemical reaction producing the afore-mentioned nitrosamines, which are extremely carcinogenic. This reaction is restricted by a number of metabolic parameters serving as biochemical protection, however, so that the risk would appear to be limited. One of the powerful inhibitors of nitrosation in the organism is ascorbic acid, vitamin C.

So far we have only mentioned the possibilities of acute poisoning by plant constituents, without considering the factors which promote or trigger the long-term toxic effects of such poisons.

For example, some plant constituents have a co-carcinogenic effect, in other words, they accelerate the development of tumours without themselves being carcinogenic. Conversely, it has been discovered that chemically related compounds can inhibit the formation of tumours. The work leading to this discovery began in 1941 with an experiment on animals by the pathologist Isaac Berenblum. He painted the shaved skin of mice with solutions of different concentrations of a known carcinogenic hydrocarbon, and calculated the borderline dose at which cancer was not initiated the first time, but only after the carcinogen had been applied several times, i.e. after chronic administration. But this was only one part of the experiment. At a later stage he examined the inflammatory influence of croton oil, a seed oil from *Croton tiglium*, a member of the spurge family (Euphorbiaceae), because at that time it was assumed that inflammation was an early stage of cancer. Surprisingly enough, he discovered that the inflammation never resulted in tumours, but that these grew on a mouse's skin when subcarcinogenic amounts of hydrocarbon were applied, followed by croton oil. From these facts it could be concluded that there are substances which are carcinogenic on their own, and others which are not, but which amplify considerably the cell damage done by the former. In 1966 Professor Erich Hecker and his colleagues at the German cancer research centre in Heidelberg examined in closer detail the results of these croton oil experiments. The active principles they isolated were fourteen diesters of a previously unknown four-ring system (tigliane), from which the polyvalent alcohol phorbol is derived, and in experiments on animals they proved its extremely co-carcinogenic effects beyond all doubt.

Once this had been established, studies began to be made of a large number of Euphorbiaceae, some of which form the basis for medicaments and foodstuffs, but which are also used for animal feed, as house plants and as a source of oil. It was discovered that only a few members of this family contained substances which presented a risk of cancer. But some worrying facts were also established, for example from the Caribbean island of Curaçao, where a tea is made from the aromatic spurge plant *Croton flavens*. It contains active co-carcinogens, which might explain the above-average incidence of cancer of the gullet on the island.

Many other plant families are currently being examined for co-carcinogenic effects. A study of the berries of the Central European spurge laurel *(Daphne mezereum)*, for instance, revealed that it contains mezerein, a co-carcinogenic skin irritant. The spurge laurel

is also highly toxic in its acute effects (the mortality rate for poison victims is thirty percent), and ten to twelve berries can be lethal for children. There are descriptions in the toxicological literature of poisoning which has occurred after the consumption of fieldfares which had fed on the berries of the spurge laurel.

In his *Allgemeine Geschichte der Pflanzengifte* (General history of the vegetable poisons), the naturalist Johann Friedrich Gmelin writes about the effects of the spurge laurel as follows: "All parts of this shrub ... especially the berries, are uncommonly poisonous, and when laid on the skin they cause redness and blisters, but when

they are swallowed they cause a terrible, long-lasting burning in the mouth, throat and gullet, and often inflammation of these areas, an unquenchable thirst, extremely violent vomiting, long-lasting, tedious and excruciating discharges from the stomach, stomach pains, which remain long after the other symptoms have disappeared, insomnia, high temperature, indescribable weakness, peeling of the epidermis all over the body, and not infrequently death. Even the scent of the flow-

ers can sometimes induce unconsciousness in closed rooms. Even the smoke from the wood, in which they had smoked their meat, killed some soldiers in Corsica after they had suffered convulsions and a terrible sensation as if they were being strangled."

Of the twenty or so co-carcinogens of widely varying structures which are known today, the phorbol diesters are the most powerful by far. Synthetically produced and modified phorbol derivatives which do not irritate the skin are currently being tested for their ability to inhibit tumours.

Substances which are carcinogenic on their own are also found in the plant world, however, and can endanger health if eaten or otherwise consumed over a period of time. A lubricating and fuel oil, obtained from the seeds of *Argemone mexicana* of the poppy family (Papaveraceae), in India, was often added illegally to edible oils. Examinations showed that sanguinarine, the main alkaloid which it contains, can cause the formation of local tumours. Nut kernels of the genus *Cycas*, which are consumed as palm sago in tropical countries, for instance on the Pacific islands, contain glycosidically bound cycasin, which has been shown in experiments on animals to be carcinogenic.

Some essential oils contain poisons which appear harmless at first sight, but which have dangerous long-term effects. Safrole, for example, which is found in many essential oils—e.g. cinnamon oil, Japanese anise oil and in particular sassafras oil—, was shown in animal tests to be a carcinogen. Nothing is yet known about any harm caused by it to the human organism. Safrole and its derivatives are currently used in a number of ways to produce perfumes, medicaments and insecticides. Trimethoxycinnamaldehyde, which is found in many commercial timbers, has the basic structure of a phenylpropane—as does safrole—, and has lately been connected with nasal carcinoma occurring with increasing frequency among lumbermen.

Poison in the animal kingdom

(Poisonous animals and animal poisons)

Animals which produce toxic substances, usually in special glands, whether to catch prey, or for specific biological or ecological purposes, to ensure survival in a particular environment—e.g. to prevent their being eaten, to protect their young, and to protect against microorganisms and other pathogens—are said to be of a primary toxic nature.

According to the specific function of a poison—whether it is to catch prey, defend the animal or its young, or whatever other reason—, the "technique" used differs from species to species. It is sometimes sufficient for the body surface to be moistened with toxic or unpleasant-tasting secretions or excretions. This is the case, for instance, with a number of toads, as well as with snails and greenfly larvae. These animals are described as "passively poisonous". Actively poisonous animals, on the other hand, generally use their toxic apparatus to catch prey by paralyzing or killing their victim.

There are also animals of a secondary toxic nature, which do not actually produce any defensive substance, but which absorb poison in some form or another, e.g. through their food, without being poisoned themselves and without concentrating it in a specific organ.

It was not until the early 20th century that science began, for medicinal and pharmacological reasons, to study animal poisons. Since the early twenties, the chemistry of these poisons has also attracted scientific interest. Many of the known animal poisons are polymolecular peptides and proteins, a number of which are of enzyme character (e.g. proteases and phospholipases) with an extremely complex structure. Less well-known are the large number with different types of structure.

Animal poisons and poisonous animals played an important role in medicine even in ancient times, even if they were often clouded in mysticism or feared to an exaggerated degree. Some illnesses, for instance, were attributed to imaginary or real animals as the emissaries of "higher powers". In ancient Egypt, the snake and the worm were generally regarded as symbols of illness. In the Middle Ages, rabies was thought to be caused by a worm which was supposed to lie under the tongue. The cause of tarantism, the so-called "dancing mania", a nervous disease which, in the past, often reached epidemic proportions, was ascribed to the tarantula, a species of wolf spider which is relatively harmless to man. The dreaded smallpox was blamed on an insect sting. Superstition went to such lengths that some animals were said to be able to injure or even kill not only by biting or stinging, or as a result of their being eaten, but even just by their look, their breath and their smell. Ambroise Paré published a work in Paris in 1552 in which the strangest illustrations can be found, including one of a crowned basilisk, which "is said to be the king of all snakes and whose head is adorned with a diamond". Its breath was supposed not only to be lethal to man, but was even said to make plants wither. Nikander reported from the pre-Christian period (*Theriaca*, lines 805–836) that the sting of the stingray (Dasyatidae family) not only inflicted painful wounds, but also made all roots and leaves die if it was bored into a tree trunk, "as if the sun had parched it with its rays … even if it was strong, green and flourishing. In the case of man, the flesh rots and wastes away. Legend tells how even Odysseus was afflicted by the accursed sting of the ray and thus perished."

Murder by animal poison plays a relatively minor role in history, although it is certainly practised by some primitive races. Moritz Richard Schomburgk tells how some South American tribes kill their enemies by attacking them in their sleep and stabbing the poisonous fang of an indigenous snake into or through their tongues. In Samoa it was the practice to place ray stings into the sleeping mats of people one wishes to eliminate. Cantharidine, which is obtained from several species of

the family of oil beetles (Meloidae), has played a part in the criminal history of poison abuse; the best-known is the Spanish fly *(Lytta vesicatoria)*, which is native to southern Europe and to Asia. The German pharmacopoeia of the 19th century lists this beetle in its dried form as a "cantharides" preparation. The blood and secondary glands of the male sex organs are particularly important ingredients. The inflammatory and blistering effects of the Spanish fly and its relatives on the human skin attracted the interest even of the ancient Greeks and Romans: Aristotle, Hippocrates and Pliny all described it, its healing power and its poisonous nature, as did Galen, who was personal physician to several Roman emperors. The Incas used the blood of a species of blister beetle to get rid of warts and corns. Beetles were also used as a prized aphrodisiac (without justification) in the love potions mentioned elsewhere. Thessalian women were considered to be particularly adept at preparing such potions in ancient times. In the Middle Ages too, as we have already seen, great faith was placed in the efficacy of such aids to love (cf. *Tristan and Isolde*). This belief in love potions still persists today, surprisingly enough, and appears time and again in one form or another, especially in Italy (diavolini di Napoli), France (pastilles galantes and pastilles à la Richelieu) and Britain (love powder). A glance at the personal columns of many journals shows beyond doubt that there are still plenty of shady characters and dubious firms keen to provide a public, which is only too willing to pay, with all sorts of different powders, pills and potions to "increase potency and the libido of one's partner", often with direct reference to "secret recipes from the Middle Ages which were long believed to be lost". One should not disregard the fact that such potions are often extremely dangerous, and that cases of cantharidine poisoning caused by them still occur from time to time.

Cantharidine is a powerful cytotoxin. The serious damage it causes to the kidneys is characteristic; this can result in the destruction of the entire series of tubules in this organ.

Suicide by means of animal poisons is, however, extremely rare in history. It is commonly known that

Cleopatra chose to kill herself with an asp *(Naja haje)*, the sacred serpent in the insignia of rank of the Pharaohs. According to legend, the cobra was used in ancient Egypt to carry out the death penalty, but accounts of this type of execution in Turkey have also come down to us from earlier centuries.

Lastly, poisoning has also resulted from using animals, parts of animals or extracts as medicine. In some parts of America it was usual in the 19th century to fight leprosy, diphtheria and fever with rattlesnake venom. However, these methods of treatment often had a fatal outcome.

A number of animal toxins—e.g. from bees, spiders and snakes—, if carefully selected and applied in the correct dose, can relieve or even save people from certain illnesses or poisoning in modern times. The hazy borderline between poison and medicine is demonstrated by the example of toad poisons. Although they were used by mediaeval quack doctors in their tinctures and ointments and by witches in magic potions, and laughed at initially by modern man, the use of dried toads actually does have a genuine pharmaceutical and chemical basis. In 17th and 18th-century Europe, secretions of the common toad *(Bufo bufo)* were used in heart therapy. Digitalis glycosides (see p. 106) were unknown at that time. Chemists first isolated the actual cardioactive principle from toad poison in 1902 and called it bufotalin, in analogy to digitalin. We know today that the most important principles are steroids such as bufotalin and bufotoxin. They also include various catechol amines such as adrenalin, noradrenalin and dopamine, as well as indole alkylamines (e.g. bufotenine, a 5-hydroxy-N,N-dimethyltryptamine), which act as tetanic poisons.

One particularly interesting compound is O-methylbufotenine from the North American Colorado toad *(Bufo alvarius)*, which is one of the strongest hallucinogens currently known. Bufotenines with a similar chem-

ical make-up are extracted by South American Indians from certain types of fungus and used as a narcotic (cf. p. 27).

During his examination in 1871 of the thickened sap of the upas *(Antiaris toxicaria)*, a mulberry tree found on Java, Kalimantan and other islands, which is used by the natives as an effective arrow poison, Domenico Fornara discovered that it had no effect on toads. Other researchers had made similar discoveries before him when experimenting with the constituents of the foxglove *(Digitalis sp.)*. The constituents of these plants closely resemble toad poisons chemically and pharmacologically—poisons which the toads themselves are resistent to.

But even the highly-toxic skin secretions of some species of toad do not always deter all of their enemies. American racoons, for instance, have learned to catch the Colorado toad on its spawning grounds, to turn it on its back and to slit open the belly. The racoon can then eat the insides of the toad (which grows up to 18 cm long and whose poison can kill a large dog) without coming into contact with its skin.

Occasionally people are poisoned in South American regions by the spawn of the aga toad *(Bufo marinus)*, which grows up to 25 cm long and is sometimes used for pest control in sugar cane plantations. This occurs when they confuse the spawn with frog spawn, which is often eaten as "mock caviar" in South America.

Other extremely poisonous animals can be found in the order of anurans (Urodela), especially in the genera *Salamandra, Triturus* and *Taricha,* although these are very rarely known to poison man. The purpose of these poisons is partly to repel the creature's natural enemies, but mainly to protect against microorganisms which would otherwise find an ideal breeding ground in the skin slime (which must be kept moist constantly to ensure that the skin can breathe). For a long time it was unclear for which enemies these poisons were intended, but recently it was finally discovered that skin necrosis rapidly forms on "detoxicated" salamanders, resulting in the death of the animals after a few days. The range of poisons found in amphibians is remarkably wide. These include heart, muscle and nerve poisons, poisons which lower or raise the blood pressure, and even local anaesthetics and hallucinogens—a veritable cocktail, indeed.

Salamanders were steeped in legend even in ancient times. In the *Theriaca* (lines 805–836), Nikander warns of the allegedly underhand nature and invariably dangerous bite of the salamander, which "even if his path takes him through blazing fire will run through it without effort and without being burnt, without the burning flames harming his cracked skin or even the extremities of his limbs" (hence the German name "fire salamander"). Pliny embellished Nikander's words even more by describing the salamander as an extremely dangerous and poisonous animal which could kill entire peoples and could poison all the fruit on a tree.

Newts of the genera *Taricha* and *Triturus* are related to the salamanders. At Stanford University it was proven that the Californian newt *(Taricha torosa)* produces the same poison—tetrodotoxin—as the puffer-fish (see p.116). European newts, for example the Alpine newt *(Triturus alpestris),* produce a secretion which is not fully understood, but which is very enzymatic in nature and causes blood decomposition.

The use of animal poisons as arrow poisons—as practised by a number of primitive peoples—was not unknown to the Greeks, because Ovid tells us (Metamorphoses, IX, 158) how the arrows of Hercules were tipped with the poison of the Lernaean hydra. In some African tribes it was customary to crush red ants underfoot and use them as an arrow poison.

African Bushmen still use the larvae of various plant-eating arrow poison beetles (e.g. *Diamphidia simplex*) as a reliable and deadly weapon. The toxins in these beetles probably originate in their food, because their hosts are members of the myrrh and mango families, of whose constituents, however, little is yet known.

The blowpipes of the Chocó Indians in the jungles of northwestern Colombia are highly effective hunting and battle weapons. The Indians produce the poison they use from strikingly-coloured frogs of the tree-climbing frog family Dendrobatidae, which they call "kokoa". The first European to note their extremely high toxicity was probably the Spanish physician Arango Posada, when he met the Chocó Indians on an expedition to Colombia in 1869. Many species of the genera *Phyllobates* and *Dendrobates* of this family, also known as arrow poison frogs, are found in Central and tropical South America. The Indians are so afraid of the poison that they never touch it with their bare hands. To catch the frogs, they imitate their calls, then seize the animals carefully with leaves and impale them on twigs. They are then "roasted" over an open fire according to an ancient ritual, which causes them to exude a milky-white fluid. Fifty blowpipe darts can be turned into highly-toxic weapons from the secretion of a single frog, each dart being treated with only about 200 µg of the toxin. If an animal is hit by one of these darts, it is paralyzed in an instant and dies within a few minutes. Since the poison is harmless if taken orally, the flesh can be eaten with impunity. The Indians immediately cut out the area around the entry point of the dart.

It was not until 1962 that an expedition succeeded in bringing back a sufficient quantity of the poison from the North Colombian jungle for scientific experiments to be carried out, thus allowing its mechanisms of action and chemical structure to be examined. Four highly poisonous steroid alkaloids (including batrachotoxin) were isolated from *Phyllobates aurotenia* (sometimes also known as *Phyllobates bicolor*).

Apart from arrows and blowpipes, animal poisons have been used in other ways for hunting. In the South Seas, the natives use extracts of the sea cucumber (of the Holothuriodea family) to catch fish: the paralyzed fish float to the surface of the water, where they can be collected. These interesting sea creatures, which are between 3 and 30 cm long, consist of muscular body walls with a cloaca and a mouth opening, surrounded by small tentacles. The "skeleton" comprises microscopically small calcareous ossicles which are imbedded in the skin. Apart from being passively poisonous by releasing toxin through the skin, various species of *Holothuria* are armed with a strange poisonous device known as the Cuvierian tubules—up to one hundred and fifty white or red threads between 10 and 20 cm long and 1 and 2 cm thick at the base of the respiratory trees, which are ejected in a bunch through the anus if the creature is attacked. They stick fast to the enemy, and can be expanded to thirty times their original size. If these poisonous organs do not suffice to repel the enemy, the sea cucumber can discharge its entire digestive tract, and thus render the foe harmless. The Cuvierian tubules and digestive tract can be regenerated within about ten to twenty-five days. The effect of this defensive reaction on fish can range from paralysis to death. Recent studies have shown this secretion to act as a nerve poison, in a similar way to cocaine. It also has a powerful haemolytic effect. In chemical terms it is a complex mixture of sulphate ester glycosides with various steroid or triterpene molecules in the sugar component (e.g. holothurinogenin). However, the toxin's ability to inhibit the spread of cancer, which was discovered only in recent years, is of particular interest. The survival time of mice infected with tumour cells doubled after treatment with holothurin. In some cases, the tumour cells even disappeared altogether. Naturally, the findings of such experiments on animals cannot be generalized or applied to humans straight away.

Smoked or dried sea cucumbers are a popular dish in southern Japan, Indonesia and the Philippines. If the digestive tract and skin are not completely removed during preparation, serious paralysis can occur, resulting in death.

Serious poisoning can also ensue after eating other sea creatures. Some globefish or puffer-fish from the family of Tetraodontidae, which live in eastern Asia and the Pacific, are particularly feared. The Japanese know them as "fugu". These fish owe their name to their ability to puff up into a ball by swallowing air or water in dangerous situations. The fugu, which contains highly-toxic tetrodotoxin in its ovaries, liver, brain and roe, is a particular delicacy in Japan. Its blood and flesh are innocuous. Gourmets claim that the fish tastes best in the early summer, when the fugu is at its most poisonous. According to Japanese statistics, several hundred cases of poisoning a year occurred between 1886 and the 1960s, fifty to sixty percent of which ended in death. The mortality rate has dropped since 1969. This is probably because restaurants must now obtain a licence to sell fugu dishes. The liver, ovaries, roe and entrails are carefully removed, so poisoning seldom occurs in such special restaurants. The chefs in charge of preparing the dish must first pass a test of their competence.

The toxin is rapidly absorbed by the human organism—some of it probably through the mucous membranes of the mouth—, and after five to thirty minutes the symptoms of poisoning set in; general weakness followed by numbness of the palate, fingers and other extremities, and difficulty in speaking. The muscles are eventually completely paralyzed, and death results from respiratory failure.

Alongside saxitoxin, which is found in some species of bivalve, fugu poison is one of the most powerful non-peptidic poisons, and cannot be destroyed by cooking. Its potency is apparent from the fact that a ton of fugu ovaries are needed to produce just 10 g of the toxin, and that it can paralyze the sensory and splanchnic nerves and the skeletal muscles in a dilution of as little as 1:2 million.

It should also be mentioned here that a number of other well-known fish also contain poison in their gonads and eggs, for example, the roe of the barbel (Barbus barbus), the carp (Cyprinus carpio), the tench (Tinca tinca) and the pike (Esox lucius). The toxin in barbel roe can cause severe nausea and diarrhoea, and is not destroyed by cooking.

The blood serum of eels (Anguilla sp.) and morays (Muraena sp.) is extremely toxic, whereas the flesh is not. Many cases of poisoning are known to have been caused by the European eel (Anguilla anguilla) and the European moray (Muraena helena). Eating an eel which has not been properly bled can result in paraesthesia in the mouth, general muscular weakness and respiratory failure, from which death can ensue. The proteinic poison is destroyed by heating.

Some molluscs (Mollusca) sometimes have a secondary toxic effect, especially in the case of some bivalves. They have no poison weapons and do not use the toxin either to catch prey or for defence. Gerhard Habermehl, who is probably the foremost contemporary expert on animal poisons, describes them as "accidentally poisonous", because the toxins they contain originate in their food. Bivalves feed on sea plankton, which contains toxic unicells, including a number of dinoflagellates (mastigophorous algae). Whenever such producers of toxin, such as the dinoflagellate Gonyaulax catenella, occur in large numbers off the North Atlantic coasts of Europe and America, off the Pacific coast from California to Alaska, or in Japan and South Africa, one finds cases of shellfish poisoning. Such cases have also occurred by the North Sea in the past.

Even today, it can still be dangerous to eat shellfish. Indeed, there were some two hundred serious cases of poisoning in five western European countries in October 1976, all caused by Spanish mussels (Mytilus edulis). Detailed studies showed that apart from the main poison, saxitoxin, there where other nerve poisons with similar effects, known as gonyautoxins. The main producer of poison was the dinoflagellate Gonyaulax tamarensis.

The toxic food of bivalves can multiply so greatly that one litre of sea water can contain twenty to forty million of these organisms. It is important to remember here that mussels and oysters filter their unicell nourishment from 20 to 40 litres of water per day, depending on their size. Saxitoxin, with a lethal dose of 3 μg/kg body weight, is one of the most toxic non-peptidic compounds known to toxicologists. About thirty minutes after eating contaminated shellfish, the victim experiences numbness of the lips and fingertips, followed by general paralysis; death can ensue within twelve hours. The poison works by blocking the path of impulses in the motorial and sensory nerves.

The ocean is also the home of many other creatures of a secondary toxic nature: for example, one type of fish poisoning is known as ciguatera poisoning, and often occurs at tropical latitudes between about 35°N and 34°S. This name covers all types of fish poisoning with gastro-intestinal and neurological symptoms caused by sea creatures which are normally edible but suddenly become poisonous—such as barracudas, parrot fish, sea perch and triggerfish. People poisoned in this way suffer an extremely painful burning sensation in the mouth, and cry out in their agony. The poison responsible is known as ciguatoxin. It is presumed to come from a species of dinoflagellate, *Gambierdiscus toxicus*, which is found particularly frequently in areas where increased cases of such poisoning occur.

New phenomena are constantly being discovered in this area. For example, it was discovered that a species of plaice which lives in the Red Sea *(Pardachirus marmoratus)* expels a milky poison from some two hundred and fifty glands on the dorsal and anal fins. This protects the fish against larger enemies such as sharks and barracudas by repelling them even from a long distance away. It kills smaller fish within a few minutes, even in a dilution of 1:5000.

Many animals produce poisons which are not dangerous to man, or do not seriously affect him. For example, a species of cockroach found in North America *(Eurycotis floridana)* produces the insecticide 2-hexenal. The sting of the bedbug *(Cimex lectularius)* is painful, but not dangerous. Other animals again produce their poisons in such a composition and dose that they can have a therapeutic effect on humans: one such example is the leech *(Hirudo medicinalis)*, whose "poison" is an anti-coagulant.

Many toxic "constituents" or secretions of animals are only poisonous to man or other mammals if they are administered to the relevant organism in an unnatural way for the purpose of experimentation, for example, if they are injected subcutaneously or intravenously: in such cases, merely touching the animal concerned would not be dangerous.

Let us now consider a few examples of poisonous animals which can be extremely dangerous to man.

We should not underestimate the danger which lurks in tropical and subtropical waters for swimmers and divers. Typical examples of this are cnidaria (polyps and jellyfish) which, with a few exceptions, are found mainly between 45°N and 30°S. The cnidaria's weaponry comprises capsules on the tentacles (nematocysts), which are fired into the skin of the "enemy" on contact, causing the venom to be expelled and paralyze the victim. The effect on man ranges from slight skin irritation to death by respiratory failure.

Cubomedusae (fire jellyfish) are the most dangerous examples, in particular the sea wasp *(Chironex fleckeri)*, which is probably the most dangerous marine creature of all. These jellyfish, which are some 20 cm in size, light blue and transparent, are difficult to see, especially as their tentacles are often several metres long. If a diver or swimmer comes into contact with one of these, it is impossible to save him, because death ensues in seconds, or minutes at the longest, caused mainly by cardio-active toxins. The poisonous principle is a protein with a molecular weight of about 150,000. Kinins and histamine cause the severe pain which is experienced. At certain times of the year, large numbers of sea wasps appear, and this sometimes means that large beaches have to be closed to bathers. The Portuguese man-of-war *(Physalia physalis)* is a dangerous polyp. The red stinging jellyfish *(Cyanea capillata)*, which is native to the North Sea, the Baltic and the Mediterranean, is yet another species which is dangerous to man.

It is interesting to note that sea turtles are immune to cnidarian venom taken orally, and can quite happily eat the Portuguese man-of-war, for instance. Sea slugs of the Aeolididae family consume unexploded jellyfish nematocysts for protection, storing them in special dorsal swellings.

Even pretty sea anemones produce cnidarian venom. These are very powerful toxins, even if they cause "only" local skin irritation and burns to man.

Apart from the sea cucumber, which we have already discussed, other marine echinoderms include actively poisonous star fish (Asteroidea). They secrete a slime through epidermis glands which can cause dermatitis in man, and sickness and paralysis if it penetrates the body (e.g. through wounds). The toxins are steroid glycosides. Their structure has been explained only in recent years, for example dihydromarthasterone.

The purpose of these poisons is to paralyze the adductor muscles of shellfish, which is the favourite food of the star fish, causing the shells to open and providing easy access to the food inside.

The crown of thorns starfish (Acanthaster planci), which is native to the Indian Ocean and the western Pacific, and which has many arms covered in long poisonous spines, can be very dangerous to man. Injuries result in serious swelling, nausea and vomiting.

The weever fish (Trachinidae), scorpion fish (Scorpaenidae) and stingray (Dasyatidae) are all actively poisonous, but most toxic fish are only passively poisonous or have only a secondary toxic effect.

The best known actively poisonous fish is the stingray, whose tail ends in a sting armed with a poison gland. The species which is sometimes found in the North Sea (Dasyatis pastinaca) is equipped with a weapon of this kind.

The stings of tropical stingrays are used by the natives as tips for their poisoned arrows. The symptoms of poisoning range from severe pain, disintegration of the upper layers of skin and nausea, to loss of consciousness, a fall in blood pressure and serious breathing difficulties, but death seldom ensues.

Even highly-prized commercial fish sometimes have active poison devices, one example being the greater weever (Trachinus draco), which is distributed in the North Sea and the Mediterranean. The short first dorsal fin and the gill-cover are armed with sharp poisonous spikes, which are not immediately apparent to the uninitiated. A burning pain is felt around the wound, which reddens and swells; the lymph glands also swell. These symptoms abate only after several days.

According to Gerhard Habermehl some fifty thousand people are poisoned every year by sea creatures, not counting the twenty thousand or so cases which arise from eating poisonous creatures. The number of fatalities runs to about three hundred.

According to estimates made in the specialist literature, the number of people who die from animal poisons every year far exceeds one hundred and fifty thousand. People are at risk, firstly if they are attacked by poisonous animals which regard them as enemies—e.g. snakes—, and secondly if they eat poisonous animals, whether in ignorance or through carelessness.

It is mainly in warmer climates that one comes into contact with various types of arthropods, in particular scorpions, spiders and insects—including bees, wasps, hornets and ants. In Central Europe we encounter bees, wasps and hornets, whose toxins are very similar both chemically and toxicologically. One member of the Hymenoptera which has been closely studied is the honey bee (Apis mellifera). The females have a sting which is modified from the egg-laying organ (ovipositor). Nearly everyone has experienced the painful swellings that such stings can cause. However, several thousand stings would normally be required to kill a man: the LD_{50} value for mice (taken intravenously is about 6mg/kg, and the amount of toxin in a sting is

In past centuries, the most hazardous experiments with animal poisons were sometimes attempted for medical purposes—an alchemist "processing" a scorpion.
Martin Johann Schmidt *The alchemist*. Copperplate engraving, 18th century.

about 0.1 mg (dry matter). Nevertheless, deaths are known to have resulted from bee stings in Europe and America on frequent occasions. These stings can be fatal for people who exhibit an allergic reaction to bee poison, as is not uncommonly the case. In such cases, stinging produces symptoms of anaphylactic shock— total circulatory failure. Bees, wasps and hornets are the leading killers, responsible for approximately one hundred thousand fatalities a year, out of some five million incidents. Bee toxin is not consistent in its make-up. It comprises enzymes, which are proteins, active basic peptides, a proteinase inhibitor and the biogenic amine histamine. Melittin, which consists of twenty-six amino acid components, is the most important of the toxic peptides, representing the main component of the bee toxin with fifty percent of the dry matter. The biogenic amine histamine is responsible for dilating the blood vessels and causing pain, and is also largely to blame for the inflammation around the sting.

Bee poison was known even in ancient Egypt as a therapeutic agent, and it was later recommended as such by Galen and Paracelsus. For a long time, sufferers from rheumatism had themselves stung by bees, sometimes with very successful results. This is no longer necessary today, because in the 1930s purified and standardized bee toxin appeared on the market in an effective ointment form. Producing bee toxin is slow work: some fifteen thousand bees are required to produce 1 g of poison.

The Crusaders are traditionally supposed to have been thrown into disarray during the siege of Massa when bee hives were thrown at them. Many such descriptions can be found in literature on the history of toxicology of such early forms of "chemical warfare".

Poisonous honey was known in some areas of Asia Minor even in ancient times. This has nothing to do with the toxicity of bee poison, however, but rather with the plants sought out by the bees, for instance some species of rhododendron (e.g. *Rhododendron ponticum*), whose toxic diterpenes (such as andromedotoxin = Acetylandromedol) end up in the honey along with the nectar. In Turkey, a number of people have been poisoned by azalea honey. Andromedotoxin, which has a similar effect to atropine, was held responsible.

Wasp poison also contains serotonin, and hornet poison serotonin and five percent acetylcholine; no animal substances are known to contain greater quantities. The pain caused by histamine and acetylcholine together is much greater than that caused by the individual components. Acetylcholine is responsible for the cardioactive effect of hornet poison.

Many genera and species of ants, which are also arthropods, produce poisons which, while they are certainly very diverse on occasion, are harmless to man except in a few cases, such as that of the tropical fire ant *(Solenopsis)*. Its stings are extremely painful, and have a more serious effect than those of bees or hornets. They produce symptoms such as fever, inflammation and paralysis. In the United States, the toxins of various fire ants have been examined, and alkaloids or alkaloid mixtures with piperidine and pyrrolidine elements have been found. It is only in recent years that the toxin of the North American harvester ant *(Pogonomyrmex badius)* has been studied in greater detail. Its sting can seriously affect even a strong man for a short time, resulting in symptoms ranging from local pain and flushing to swelling of the lymph glands and perspiration. This is the most active of insect poisons, being even more effective than that of the hornet. It contains large concentrations of the enzymes phospholipase A and B, hyaluronidase, acidic phosphatases, lipases and esterases. It can cause haemolysis (breaking up of the blood corpuscles) even in a dilution of 4 µg/ml.

Let us now turn to the scorpion, of which there are some six hundred and fifty species in the animal kingdom. Scorpions are arachnids: they are estimated to be

The spawn of the aga toad *(Bufo marinus)*, which can grow up to 25 cm long, is sometimes responsible for cases of poisoning in South America. This occurs when it is eaten instead of frog spawn, which is often consumed as "mock caviar".

Alkaloids with very different chemical properties are found in species of *Dendrobates*, for instance the only animal compound with C-C-triple bonds in the histrionicotoxin found in *Dendrobates histrionicus*.

The spotted salamander *(Salamandra salamandra)* was steeped in legend in ancient times, and was considered extremely cunning and treacherous. Its toxic skin secretions, however, are not dangerous to man.

Newts of the genus *Triturus* produce skin secretions which are highly enzymatic and have a haemolytic effect.
Alpine newts *(Triturus alpestris apuanus)*.

Some representatives of the molluscs, in particular mussels, can have a secondary toxic effect if they consume dinoflagellates contaminated with saxitoxin.

Porcupine fish (Diodontidae) and puffer-fish (Tetraodontidae) produce highly-toxic tetrodotoxin in their livers, brains and gonads. Many fatalities have occurred in Asia as a result of incorrect preparation of this fish as the gourmet dish "fugu".
Naturkundemuseum, Leipzig.

Even pretty sea anemones (*Radianthus* sp.) produce cnidarian venoms which can irritate the human skin and stun fish. However, they serve as hosts to the clown fish *(Amphiprion bicinctus)*, which constantly keeps the anemone clean.

The crown of thorns starfish *(Acanthaster planci)* can paralyze the adductor muscles of bivalves, its favourite food, causing the shells to open. If humans come into contact with it, they can suffer from dermatitis or even paralysis.

The red firefish *(Pterois volitans)* and the zebra fish *(Pterois lunalus)* illustrated here, which are both members of the family of scorpion fish, can endanger divers and bathers in tropical seas. The characteristic symptoms of poisoning are severe local pain and inflammation, followed sometimes by faintness and nausea, and on rare occasions collapse. The structure of the toxin is not yet fully understood, but it is highly likely that a protein is involved.

Despite its pleasant taste, the greater weever *(Trachinus draco)*, which is armed with poisonous spines, used to be thrown back into the sea by North Sea fishermen as an offering to St. Peter.

Most of the 25,000 or so species of spider are poisonous, but the representatives of only a few families are dangerous to man. Species of *Avicularia*, from the family of bird spiders—which, on the whole, are not very poisonous—can cause large, deep wounds with their bites.

The black widow *(Latrodectus mactans)*, a theridiid spider, is a particularly aggressive poisonous species.

The largest scorpion known today is *Pandinus imperator*, which is native to equatorial Africa, and grows up to 18 cm long.

People who suffer from an allergy to bee stings can, in certain circumstances, be exposed to great danger by just one sting from a honey bee *(Apis mellifera)*.

Animal poisons have rarely been used in the past for murders and suicides. Nonetheless, the suicide of the last Egyptian queen, Cleopatra VII, the mistress of Julius Caesar and Mark Antony, has gone down in history. Vanquished by Octavianus, she killed herself with an asp, or Egyptian cobra. Peter Paul Rubens, *The death of Cleopatra*. Národní Galeri, Prague.

Snake venom can vary considerably in its mechanism of action. Different compositions of venom can even be found within a single species. Prairie rattlesnake *(Crotalus viridis)*.

Extracting the venom from a black mamba *(Dendroaspis polylepis)* at the Snake Farm, Lake Baringo, Kenya.

About one in three cobra bites *(Naja naja)* is lethal.

The puff adder *(Bitis arietans)*, which is indigenous to the African continent, is one of the most feared of all vipers.

Sea snakes (Hydrophiidae) are poisonous without exception—their bites are lethal.

The aggressive American coral snakes *(Micrurus corallinus)* are venemous snakes whose bites are fatal in ten to twenty percent of cases.

Venereal disease in the form of epidemic syphilis was a common result of prostitution and immorality in bathhouses. Paracelsus treated this with mercury finely distributed in pig fat. This treatment must have resulted, not infrequently, in poisoning.

Bathhouse. Miniature from: Valerius Maximus, pre-1480. Universitätsbibliothek, Leipzig.

Over the centuries, arsenic gained a notorious reputation as the "poison of poisons". It is obtained by heating natural arsenic minerals.

Spectacles have been made from beryllium since the 12th century, and today, beryllium and its compounds are irreplaceable materials. Because of its toxicity, strict safety measures govern its processing.

In past centuries, the most hazardous experiments with animal poisons were sometimes attempted for medical purposes—an alchemist "processing" a scorpion.
Martin Johann Schmid, *The alchemist.* Copperplate engraving, 18th century.

responsible for some five thousand deaths all over the world out of a total of five hundred thousand incidents every year. Apart from a few species which are extremely dangerous to man, there are other harmless species, and the general fear with which scorpions are regarded is probably exaggerated. *Androctonus australis* and *Leiurus quinquestriatus* are responsible for ninety-five percent of all fatalities from scorpion stings in Northwest Africa. The poison of the *Androctonus* comprises up to seven short-chain proteins and enzymes.

It was doubtless the ugly, repugnant and terrifying appearance of many spiders which contributed to the creation of "toxicological fables", even in ancient times, which often branded perfectly harmless spiders as extremely dangerous poisonous creatures. Spiders use their toxins exclusively for killing their prey. The toxins of the individual species have very different compositions. Apart from biogenic amines and enzymes they also contain powerful neurotoxic polypeptides. Although most of the twenty-five thousand species are indeed poisonous, only a few of these, and then only those which live in warmer climates, present any serious threat to humans. In Brazil, the eastern Mediterranean and Yugoslavia, spiders sometimes occur in such numbers that they present almost as big a problem as snakes.

The black widow spider *(Latrodectus mactans)* and a species of comb spider *(Phoneutria fera)* are considered particularly aggressive. Theridiid spiders of the genus *Latrodectus* are native to America, Southwest Africa and Europe, and species of *Phoneutria* live in South America, in particular Brazil. Individual specimens of the comb spider have sometimes been brought to Europe in banana boxes. Adults can recover from its bite after about forty-eight hours, but it is often lethal for children. The symptoms are a burning pain, an increased pulse rate, fever, nausea, vomiting, blindness and breathing difficulties. Death results from respiratory failure.

One species which is feared in the Mediterranean area and in Asia is the malmignatte *(Latrodectus mactans tredecimguttatus)*, known in the Soviet Union as the karakurt. Symptoms of poisoning are severe headaches, bilious vomiting, and very severe pains in the bones, which return periodically. In serious cases, death can ensue.

In the 19th century there were often plagues of malmignattes, and great damage was done to the stocks of cattle on the Lower Volga by these infestations.

The only dangerous spider found in Germany (in the Odenwald and in Rhenish Hesse) is *Chiracanthium punctorium*, which can cause mild cases of poisoning. The affected part is extremely painful, turns blue-red in colour and swells. Shivering and tightness in the chest can occur. Children experience nausea, vomiting and headaches, as well as a slight increase in temperature. The symptoms disappear after about three days, although the affected part remains red and swollen for longer, and sometimes begins to fester.

The tarantula *(Lycosa tarantula)* which lives in Italy and Spain, and is named after the town of Taranto, is not very dangerous; its bite "only" causes necrosis. Until the 18th century, long spirited dances—tarantellas—were recommended as a form of treatment.

Today, there are spider farms all over the world which produce spider toxins—e.g. that of the black widow—for therapeutic purposes, such as the treatment of rheumatism. Even in the 19th century, spider preparations were being used for healing, although the methods of treatment used were sometimes very dubious.

People have always considered the snake as the most dangerous, indeed the quintessential poisonous animal. One might say that snake venom is the "classic" animal poison. One reason for this may be that Cleopatra VII, the mistress of Caesar and Marcus Antonius, committed suicide by means of a snake bite. Snake bites and their treatment are discussed at length in the ancient medical writings of the Indians, Egyptians, Arabians, Persians, Greeks and Romans, almost certainly inspired by the frequency of such poisoning in warmer climes where snakes flourish. Snakes also play an extremely important role in the religions and myths of these peoples, where fact is usually mingled with dark superstition. Herodotus described winged serpents, Aristotle thought that if one gouged out the eyes or cut off the tail of a snake, these would regenerate, and Aelian described a purple snake which did not bite, but spat at its enemy, causing the affected part to rot.

It was not until 1664 that the Italian physician Francesco Redi proved in an experiment on himself that it is completely harmless to drink snake venom as long as the gastro-intestinal tract is in no way injured or ulcerated. Because of its proteinaceous nature, the venom can only take effect if it is introduced directly into the body tissue. Curative powers of snake venom were discovered at an early time. One of the oldest documents

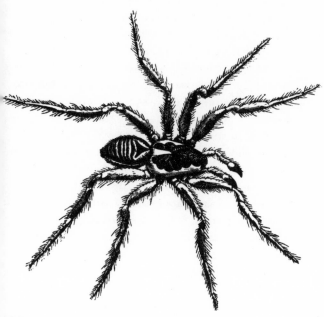

relating to this subject dates back to 2500 B.C., and originated in India. So-called "snake fat" still plays a part in popular medicine today as a cure for rheumatism. A preparation called "axungia viperarum" found its way into the *Pharmacopoea Wirtembergica* in 1760. In the 19th century, homoeopathic medicine used snake venom practically as a panacea.

Nowadays snake venom is used as a therapeutic agent in the form of an ointment in non-specific stimulation therapy to alleviate rheumatism, sciatica and chronic arthritis. Preparations of the venom of some snakes (e.g. some viper venoms) are used to promote blood clotting (e.g. in cases of haemophilia—, while others, such as that of the Malaysian moccasin *(Agkistrodon rhodostoma)* are used to remove blood clots.

Until about 1960, when no other psychopharmacological drugs were available, preparations from the South American rattlesnake *(Crotalus durissus terrificus)* were used to treat epileptics, with a large degree of success.

The snake venoms which are commercially available in preparations today contain standardized ingredients in accordance with strict guidelines set down in the pharmacopoeia. But one must remember that snake venom has been produced as a pure substance for less than fifty years. It was in 1938 that the first special snake toxin was isolated, using the venom of the South American rattlesnake.

At about the same time a neurotoxin, which would nowadays be considered impure, was isolated from cobra venom. In 1965 the venom of the Chinese cobra *(Naja naja atra)* was isolated. Snake venom is now produced in so-called "snake farms" for pharmaceutical purposes by massaging and electrically stimulating the poison glands of the snakes. If kept in a dry, dark place, the dried white, yellow or greenish powder will remain effective for several years. Ninety to ninety-five percent of this dried poison is made up of polypeptides and proteins of different toxicity and modes of action, of non-toxic proteins and of proteins with enzymatic properties. It also contains very small quantities of other organic compounds—free amino acids, low-molecular peptides, nucleotides, carbohydrates, lipids and biogenic amines—and metals, e.g. calcium, zinc, manganese, sodium and potassium.

The best known are the neurotoxins, which affect the nervous system. They are transmitted by poisonous adder and sea snake bites. These are low-molecular basic proteins, consisting of about sixty to seventy-four amino acids which, because of their relatively small molecular size, can spread extremely quickly through the tissue of the victim.

Most neurotoxins prevent the transmission of stimuli from the nerve endings to the muscles, causing symptoms of paralysis in victims bitten by such snakes. Viper and pit viper venom has a low neurotoxin content, but contains large quantities of cytotoxins. These are polymolecular basic proteins which spread only slowly through the tissue, and thus initially cause severe local poisoning (necrosis). The cytotoxins have a poisonous effect on many cell types (e.g. the red corpuscles) by destroying their cell membranes.

Pit vipers in particular also have elements in their venom which trigger a degeneration of the muscle fibres. Necrosis of the kidney tubules, on the other hand, is caused by the nephrotoxins found in the venom of the sea snake and other species.

Other poisons include the cardiotoxins of adders which, as their name suggests, have a harmful effect on the heart, although in some cases they also cause general cell damage.

The effectiveness of a snake venom depends on the amount of venom contained in the bite, its strength, and, of course, the species of snake, how often it bites, its sex, its state of health and even its mental state, but it also depends on the size and age of the snake, climatic conditions, the ambient temperature, the time of year and even of day, and of course where the victim is bitten. It is extremely important whether a muscle or a blood vessel is bitten. The toxins reach the heart and brain much more rapidly via the blood vessels, so that in certain circumstances even the bite of the common adder (Vipera berus) can be lethal.

The sand viper (Vipera ammodytes), which is indigenous to southern Europe, is widely stocked in European snake farms. The snakes are regularly "milked", and sooner or later their supply of venom is exhausted, and they have to be replaced. Obtaining the venom is a slow process. The bite of a sand viper, for instance, contains only about 30 mg of toxic fluid, which when dried produces a residue of 10 mg. Scientific research into snake toxins is still in its infancy.

The primary structures of more than twenty-five toxins of sea snakes and adders are now known. Vipers and pit vipers have not been studied quite so closely. In general, toxic enzymes are the main element in these poisons, although their mechanisms of action are not yet understood. Genuine toxins seem to be missing in many species of viper and rattlesnake. Viper poisons, or rather the toxic enzymes they contain, cause swelling and severe pain, followed by tissue damage, circulatory disorders and cardiovascular shock. Death can result from shock, from embolism or from massive haemorrhages. One of the most dangerous and aggressive vipers is the puff adder (Bitis arietans), which lives in Africa and Arabia.

Snake venoms are the only natural products to contain these high concentrations of such extremely biologically active enzymes, which makes them very important for biochemists as parent materials for the isolation of a number of valuable enzymes.

In all, it is estimated that more than two million people are bitten by snakes every year, resulting in some seventy thousand fatalities. The average mortality rate among victims of snake bites is about 2.5 percent. Nonetheless, some snakes are much more deadly, for example the black mamba *(Dendroaspis polylepis)*, which lives in Africa and whose bite is lethal in almost one hundred percent of cases; the Indian cobra *(Naja naja)* (thirty-two percent of cases) and the aggressive American coral snake *(Micrurus* sp.) (ten to twenty percent). Then there are the aggressive saw-scaled vipers *(Echis carinatus)* which live in Northeast Africa, Arabia and India (twenty percent); the South American rattlesnake *(Crotalus durissus terrificus)* (twelve percent) and the Malaysian moccasin *(Agkistrodon rhodostoma)* (twenty percent), which is responsible for about two thirds of all snake bites in Southeast Asia.

In comparison with these, the common adder found in Central Europe *(Vipera berus)* appears relatively harmless. In Sweden, for example, there are some thirteen hundred adder bites every year, of which about twelve percent require hospitalization. The mortality rate is 0.3 percent. In the Federal Republic of Germany there were two hundred eleven accidents involving adders between 1964 and 1969, but no fatalities.

Before the introduction of snake serum, the mortality rate lay at about ten percent. Of the two hundred sixteen cases of poisoning by snake bites in the German Empire between 1883 and 1892, fourteen (i.e. 6.4 percent) proved fatal. Today, the adder has become very rare in Central Europe, because it was subjected to a campaign of mass extermination which continued into the 20th century. However, there was a veritable plague of adders until the 18th century in some areas, such as North Germany and Saxony, and it is understandable that large rewards were offered for their capture.

Before monovalent and polyvalent snake serums were developed and produced—today they are used all over the world—many more bites proved lethal than nowadays. The concept of such a serum was first developed after it was noticed in experiments that animals which did not die from snake bites became increasingly immune to a poison, the more they were exposed to it. Using this knowledge as a starting-point, in the State of Michigan, H. Sewall began a systematic immunization experiment on pigeons using rattlesnake poison. Experiments carried out in later years by numerous researchers on different animals with different snake venoms showed that the serum of an immunized animal can also protect a non-immunized animal against the effects of a snake poison. Thus snake serum was born. Because of the many successful experiments which had been carried out on animals, Albert Calmette, of the Pasteur Institute in Lille, envisaged the practical utilization of an antitoxic serum in treating snake bites. At the end of the 19th century, he succeeded, by administering gradually increasing doses of cobra poison, in immunizing horses to such an extent that they could eventually tolerate injections of 2 g of dried cobra venom, i.e. two hundred times the normal lethal dose, without reacting to it. At this stage, blood was taken from the immune animals, and from it a serum was obtained which proved to be antitoxic in test on other animals. This was the first monovalent snake serum, which was effective against the venom of the cobra and other closely related snakes. Calmette also suggested that a polyvalent serum might be developed by treating animals used for serum production with the toxins of various species of snake.

It is interesting to note that the peoples of classical Antiquity, as well as several primitive races, must already have known how to immunize people by using gradually increased doses of snake venom. Annaeus Lucanus, for instance, gives an account in *Pharsalia*, Book IX, (lines 835–878) of people who were immune to snake poisons. Furthermore, according to the oral traditions of the Hottentots, it seems to have been customary to extract and drink the contents of the venom glands of snakes they had caught. The result was said to be only a slight feeling of dizziness, and later bites are reported to have been borne with no ill-effects. Among the natives of Mexico and South America, in particular Brazil, it was the custom to protect oneself against snake bites by scratching one's skin repeatedly with poison fangs.

In 1844 Drummond Hay gave an account of a sect of snake charmers known as the Aissanas, who continually handled snakes when performing. Control tests on animals showed that these snakes were poisonous, but the snake charmers did not suffer any ill-effects from the bites which formed part of their rituals. The members quoted the supposed or actual founder of the sect, Seedna Eiser, who is said to have lived in Meknès (Morocco) in the mid-17th century. On his travels through the Sous desert, he was accompanied by many followers, and when they were hungry and cried out for

bread, he replied angrily with the usual Arab curse, "Kool sim" ("take poison"). With an unshakeable belief in their prophet, they followed his supposed advice thereafter by eating snakes and other reptiles, and this is said to have made them immune to snake venom.

Before the introduction of snake serum, treatment for snake bites was very much a hit-and-miss affair. It included such brutal measures as immediate amputation of the affected limb, cauterizing with a red-hot iron, or burning gunpowder on the affected part, as well as the external and intravenous use of ammonia, administration of strychnine or pilocarpine and the injection of oxidizing agents near the wound. Even at the beginning of this century, the use of chlorine water, potassium permanganate, chromium oxide and *eau de Javelle*—a hypochlorite solution—was recommended.

Before coming to the end of this chapter, brief mention should be made of one of the few poisonous mammals, the Australian duck-billed platypus *(Ornithorhynchus anatinus)*. The male of the species has moveable spurs on both hind legs which are crossed by fine ducts and connected to a venom gland in the hip area. As long ago as 1817, Sir John Jamieson described the effects of poisoning by the secretion of this mammal after a hunting accident. A beater at the hunt pulled an animal, which had been shot, out of the water, but it drove its spur into his hand with such force that it had to be killed before the spur could be removed. The hand swelled up at once, the inflammation rapidly spread up to his shoulder, and he suffered severe pain. The external symptoms resembled those of a snake bite. The victim was confined to his bed for several days, and it was nine weeks before he could use his hand again. Little is yet known about the chemical structure or composition of the venom, a neurotoxine rich in enzymes. This chapter on poisonous animals and animal poisons has illustrated once again just how fragmentary our concrete toxicological and chemical knowledge still is.

Deadly rocks and crystals

(Poisons in the mineral world)

The previous chapters may have given the reader the impression that poisons occur almost exclusively in the plant and animal worlds. We will now attempt to correct this impression, because inanimate material—rocks, minerals, crystals and salts—can also be biologically active vis-à-vis living organisms. Man learned thousands of years ago that some of the ores, rocks, metals and numerous salts which he used were lethal poisons, or that poisons could be obtained from them by means of simple techniques.

We have only room here to look at a few of the wide range of inorganic substances of this type.

One of the elements which might be described as a "classic" poison is arsenic, or arsenic (III) oxide. It is obtained by roasting natural arsenopyrite (FeAsS). This white, odourless powder has been produced since the 8th century. For a long time it was notorious as the "poison of poisons" and "inheritance powder".

One of the heydays in the use of arsenic was in Renaissance Italy. One only has to think of the murders by poison in the Visconti, Sforza and Medici families.

In his book *Mineral- und Pflanzengifte* (Mineral and vegetable poisons), Otto Lange writes: "It sounds like a tale from the realm of fiction when one hears that ... 'poisoners' with state concessions presented price-lists to the Doge of Venice in which set rates were offered for the prompt and efficient disposal by poisoning of important figures. Popes were cheap: it cost only one hundred ducats to get rid of them. Five hundred ducats, however, were charged for poisoning a sultan."

One of the most disreputable papal figures was Alexander VI of the Borgia family, whose son Cesare was also notorious. The main component of the infamous poisons used by the Borgias ("cantarella") was probably arsenic acid. In 1503, Alexander VI himself finally fell victim to arsenic poisoning.

At the end of the 17th century, a lady called Teofania di Adamo (Tofana) played an inglorious role in the history of Italian poisoners. When she died in Palermo, one of her "pupils", who also called herself Tofana, continued her business in Rome with the help of some female assistants. When these brewers of poison were executed, it is said that good window seats could be had for thirty ducats. But this execution did not bring an end to the era of "aqua tofana", which was a special arsenic solution. Seventy years later, a third woman calling herself Tofana stood trial in Naples. She had sent the poison to customers, some beyond the frontiers of Naples, as "manna of St. Nicholas of Bari", in glass bottles depicting the saint.

The "popularity" enjoyed by arsenic had a sound chemical and toxicological basis. Since the lethal dose had no taste or smell, it was easily administered to the victim, whilst the murderer could be sure of not being caught, at least in those days, because the symptoms of acute poisoning were almost identical to those of cholera, an extremely widespread disease in the Middle Ages. Moreover, it was not then possible to detect the substance in the body of the victim. Even as little as 0.1 g is lethal for adults. However, there are very great fluctuations from person to person in terms of sensitivity to the poison. The acute symptoms of poisoning are terrible stomach pains, a burning sensation in the throat, and vomiting. Death can occur, after considerable suffering, in twelve to eighteen hours, but often only after a few days have passed.

The situation took a turn for the worse, as far as potential arsenic murderers were concerned, in 1832, when the British chemist James Marsh was an expert witness at a trial for murder by arsenic. Marsh made a detailed study of the analytical facts about arsenic which were already known. It was his over-riding personal ambition to present visible proof of the poison to the jury. He finally found a way of achieving this, by reducing the arsenic oxide or the arsenic compound involved to gaseous arsenic trihydride using zinc and sulphuric acid. He passed this gas through a heated tube, and the arsenic formed a dark shiny deposit on a cold porcelain bowl. He published his discovery in 1836. This simple test allows quantities of arsenic as small as 0.0001 mg to be detected, a level of sensitivity which, with other elements, can only be achieved by very complicated analytical techniques. Marsh did not suspect in 1836 that his method of detecting arsenic would achieve immortality as a classic method of forensic toxicology. The simplicity and accuracy of this test are still admired today. After the introduction of the Marsh test, the number of murders by arsenic poisoning fell dramatically, although cases of arsenic poisoning do still occur from time to time. Here is an example from this century, which also demonstrates the progress that has been made by forensic chemists in detecting poison.

New methods of analysis always attract public attention when they are used to solve crimes. This was also the case with neutron-activation analysis, one of the modern methods of detecting a number of elements. In the early fifties, a certain Madame Marie Besnard stood trial in Paris on several charges of murder by arsenic poisoning. Her pedantic defence lawyers cast doubt on the classic methods of detecting arsenic. For this reason, neutron-activation analysis was used for the first time in the toxicological evidence to which the Nobel Prize winner Frédéric Joliot contributed. Despite the successful detection of the poison, Madame Besnard was eventually acquitted after the trial had dragged on for years, because it could not be proven beyond doubt that the arsenic had not, by some unknown microbiological process, contaminated the corpses from the soil in the cemetery.

Although arsenic is an extremely potent poison, doses of 0.5 to 5 mg are still used today in homoeopathy, for example to cure chlorosis, rickets, neuralgia, nervous asthma, weakness and nervous exhaustion. Doses of 0.5 to 1 mg of arsenic often used to be administered in dentistry to deaden the nerves in the teeth. The Arab doctor Abu Bakr ar-Razi recommended arsenic as a remedy for anaemia and nervous and skin diseases.

In the Middle Ages, gypsy horse dealers gave their clapped-out old nags arsenic before selling them, to give them a fiery look, smooth hair and a fuller appearance for a few hours. Ageing ladies are also said to have used this means from time to time when husband-hunting.

The best-known therapeutic application of organic arsenic compounds can be traced back to the German physician Paul Ehrlich, who created the basis for the first comprehensive and effective treatment of syphilis with his discovery of arsenic therapy and the preparation salvarsan.

Even in the 20th century there have been arsenic eaters among the mountaineers, wood-cutters and foresters of northern and northwestern Styria, in the Tyrol, and in the Salzkammergut. They took gradually increasing doses so as to be better able to cope with the exigencies of mountain life. After a relatively long period of habituation, these people could take single doses of up to 0.4g (i.e. four times the normal lethal dose). However, habituation of this type occurs only if the arsenic is taken orally. Even these people would become ill immediately if they injected themselves with only a fraction of this amount, or drank a readily soluble arsenic compound. This shows that we must be dealing with so-called absorption immunity, because the intestinal wall makes it difficult for the arsenic to be absorbed into the body.

Acute arsenic poisoning leads to widespread tissue destruction, caused by damage to the capillaries; after oral administration, the cholera-like symptoms mentioned above of sickness and diarrhoea occur. In the case of chronic arsenic poisoning, numerous metabolic processes are inhibited, and malignant tumours can develop. Thus "vintner's cancer" occurs in wine-growing areas where insects such as the vine louse are controlled by pesticides containing arsenic—a practice which is illegal in the USA and Europe nowadays. Arsenic compounds are absorbed and stored for long periods in all tissues, especially the liver, kidney, hair and nails.

This brings us to another spectacular chapter in the colourful history of arsenic.

Rumours and theories have surfaced time and again about Napoleon dying an unnatural death. His symptoms, as recorded in the accounts of eyewitnesses, suggest a combination of arsenic and mercury poisoning. Even at the Court of Louis XIV, such mixtures were a popular means of disposing of one's disagreeable contemporaries. First the victim was given amounts of arsenic over a relatively long period which, while not immediately fatal, gave rise to unspecific symptoms. As the doctor treating the victim found the symptoms very confusing, one could expect calomel to be administered in the course of treatment, a mercury(I)-chloride which was commonly used in those days as a laxative and diuretic. As calomel is practically non-toxic at first, almond milk had to be administered to the patient to achieve a toxic effect. The victim's body, already weakened by the arsenic, would then of course be unable to tolerate such a sudden dose of poison, and the patient would die without foul play ever being suspected. This is possibly what happened in the case of Napoleon. It is known that there were no bitter almonds on St. Helena at that time, and that almond milk was therefore unavailable, but this was specially procured for Napoleon on 25th April 1821. He died on 5th May. Thus it is very natural to suspect that a course of events similar to that described above was involved in the death of Napoleon. To test for mercury, however, one would have to study the mortal remains of Napoleon. What can be, and indeed has been proved without resort to these, however, is that arsenic was absorbed by his body in the years before his death.

As has already been stated, numerous elements and trace elements are stored in the hair. If one has samples of the suspected victim's hair from different periods of his life, they can be examined from the roots to the tips and, with reference to the normal growth rate of hair, very precise details can be discovered about the arsenic intake of the victim. In the case of Napoleon, such samples were fortunately available, because the emperor used to give locks of his hair to subjects as a sign of his particular favour, and they would often record the history of these locks. Furthermore, Napoleon was shaved after his death on 6th May so that a dead mask could be made, and the hair was distributed among his friends. Plenty of material was thus available for comparative analysis. One hundred and forty years after his death, samples of his hair found their way to the Institute of Forensic Medicine at the University of Glasgow, where they were bombarded with neutrons from a nuclear reactor for twenty-four hours. The activated hair emitted radioactive rays which revealed that it contained 10.38 ppm arsenic—the normal level is about 0.5 to 1.3 ppm, i.e. about ten times less. The distribution of the arsenic over a hair length of 9 cm was also studied. After evaluating all of the results, it was eventually concluded that Napoleon certainly absorbed arsenic at frequent intervals between 1816 and his death, and that the periodicity of the measured concentrations of poison corresponded with the recorded details of his case history.

Arsenic in hair samples may, however, have other causes than oral administration. In 1775 the Swedish chemist Carl Wilhelm Scheele introduced green copper arsenite as a dye: its toxicity was discovered in 1815. Most cases of poisoning resulting from the use of these dyes could be traced back to wallpaper. In 1893 it was established that arsenic was released from these wallpaper dyes as volatile trimethyl arsine in the presence of mould. Since those who suspected that Napoleon had been murdered by arsenic refused to let the matter rest, his death was examined once again a few years ago, and a piece of the wallpaper from the empereror's study, which was found in a notebook, was discovered to contain arsenic in the green parts of the pattern. Since then, other critics have cast doubt on the methods used to analyze Napoleon's hair. So more than 150 years after Napoleon's death, the chapter on "arsenic and Napoleon" is still not closed for toxicologists.

We have lingered a disproportionately long time on the history of arsenic, but it is still considered a prime example of the inorganic poisons. Let us turn now to a few examples of the many other metals or metallic compounds which present a danger to health.

It is often not known by the general public that tons of metals fall onto us from the skies with the waste gases from power stations. Various metals are also contained in the waste from the chemical and metalworking industries, sometimes in enormous quantities, and thus released into the environment. Heavy-metal ions in particular are able to form a chemical bond with SH-groups of proteins, and especially of numerous en-

zymes, which are of primary importance for the functionability of the human and of animal organisms.

Lead compounds, for instance, can inhibit porphyrin synthesis, which is essential for the formation of blood pigment, finally resulting in anaemia. Chronic lead poisoning, where small amounts are absorbed over a period of months or years, is particularly dangerous.

Lead in the form of metallic dust, or lead oxide dust, is absorbed by the mucous membranes. Lipoid-soluble lead compounds also penetrate the body through the epidermis. The organism stores the greater part of the absorbed lead in the bones, and this can result in cumulative (chronic) lead poisoning.

Lead poisoning is known to have occurred even in ancient times. White lead and minium have been used as dyes over the centuries. Organic lead compounds, such as lead acetate, were also used for medicinal purposes (e.g. lead plaster).

Mass poisoning has also been caused on occasion by the use of lead pipes for the supply of drinking water, when certain conditions, such as when water spends a long time lying in the pipes, high summer temperatures, and acid water constituents—such as humic acid, which can be found in many ground waters—, led to high concentrations of dissolved lead, as happened in Dessau in 1880 and Leipzig in 1930.

In earlier times, lead was sometimes used in millstones, which caused serious contamination of the flour and resulted in poisoning.

Lead silicates were—and still are—contained in the glaze on earthenware. Dangerous concentrations of these can be dissolved by acidic foodstuffs.

But the danger today lies almost exclusively in the products of vehicle combustion, because lead additives (tetraethyl lead) in fuel have made lead an almost ubiquitous pollutant. The demand for lead-free petrol is therefore fully justified in terms of preventive medicine and toxicology.

Cadmium is another extremely problematic element. Chronic cadmium poisoning can result in anaemia, bone defects and damage to the lungs and kidneys, as well as to germ-cells. Acute poisoning is also not infrequently caused by cadmium and its compounds, however, because many of its compounds are absorbed faster and stored more slowly than, for instance, in the case of lead and its compounds. Apart from inhibiting enzymes, cadmium attacks the biosynthesis of energy-rich phosphorous compounds, and is therefore a metabolic poison with a wide range of effects. Cadmium

compounds have also proved to be carcinogenic in animal experiments. Oral consumption of cadmium salts, which is possible if acidic foodstuffs come into contact with metal cutlery or cooking implements containing cadmium over a long period, can cause severe irritation of the stomach and intestines. As little as 40 mg of cadmium in the form of a soluble salt can be lethal. Inhaling cadmium dust or vapour causes serious pulmonary oedema and bronchopneumonia (inflammation of the lung tissue) after twelve to twenty-six hours. This is a particular risk for those welding or flame-cutting alloys containing cadmium. However, the dramatic nature of cadmium poisoning came into the limelight only after the Second World War. It has become no less than a symbol of environmental pollution in Japan. The inhabitants of some Japanese villages which lie 50 km downstream of an abandoned zinc mine were found to be up to 30 cm shorter than the norm. More detailed clinical and chemical studies proved that calcium ions were being washed out of their bones. These symptoms have since been known worldwide as "itai-itai disease". They were caused by chronic consumption of cadmium sulphate, which was washed out of the overburden dumps of the zinc mine. Signs of the disease appear only after five to ten years, and in extreme cases only after twenty-five to thirty years, by which time nothing more can be done to repair the damage.

Mercury is another poisonous element which has been causing problems for centuries. Acute poisoning by hydrogen salts results in inflammation of the stomach and large intestine, intestinal ulcers and kidney damage; chronic poisoning causes damage mainly to the nervous system. In the case of organomercury compounds, the optical nerves in particular are damaged, and blindness is one of the consequences. Mercury has been known to man from the earliest times. The first traces of it were found in a vessel that was discovered by Heinrich Schliemann, the famous German archaeologist, in an Egyptian tomb from the 16th or 15th century B.C. In Roman times most of the workers in the cinnabar mine at Almadén (Spain) were slaves; the mercury poisoning they suffered was described by Pliny as "slave's disease". Since the harmful effects of working in mercury mines were well-known, Plutarch demanded that only criminal slaves should be put to work there. Almadén still has the greatest deposit of cinnabar ore (mercuric sulphide), and is relatively rich in metal, with six percent mercury. In the 4th century, Ausonius accused Roman women, in one of his works, of using mercury to get rid of jealous husbands. In mediaeval Venice and in other parts of Europe too, hired killers used mercury vapour, which was undetectable, to dispose of undesirable contemporaries. An extremely large number of cases—some historical accounts, others legends and anecdotes—have come down to us through the years.

The large-scale production of mirrors coated with mercury began in about the 15th century, and until the mid-18th century this was the only known method of mirror production. Ramazzini gave the following account of mirror-makers on the island of Murano near Venice: "The workers gaze against their will into the mirrors they have made, seeing in them their own misery and cursing their trade." The mercury-working trade has become no less than a prototype of occupational poisoning for industrial medicine.

At the time of the French Revolution, the most popular suicide poison was mercury dichloride ($HgCl_2$), which had been known since the 5th century. In the following centuries, too, even in the first half of the 20th century, it had the reputation of being a murder and suicide poison.

Mass poisoning by mercury has also occurred. In 1803, nine hundred workers at the Yugoslavian mine in Idrija and nearby residents were afflicted by the "mercury tremors" following a pit fire. Today some two thousand tons of mercury enter the atmosphere throughout the world from the smelting of sulphidic ores, five thousand tons from the production of cement and phosphorus, and five thousand tons from burning coal and oil. Mercury pollution of rivers is also very high because of the waste products of industry, especially electrolysis plants. These figures are only selected examples of the way in which the biosphere is being polluted by mercury all over the world, whether as an element or as a salt. But organic compounds of mercury also exist. The symptoms of poisoning then differ considerably from those of elemental mercury and inorganic mercury compounds. Organic compounds of mercury have been used since about 1914 as seed protectants, and this has caused wide-scale poisoning on more than one occasion. For example, in 1972 very serious illness was suffered in Iraq after bread was eaten which had been baked from grain treated with ethyl mercury-p-toluene sulphanilide. Thus more than six thousand five hundred people were affected, of whom two hundred and sixty died. Similar cases of mass-poisoning had already occurred in Iraq in 1956 and 1960 as a result of seed treatment with mercury preparations.

So-called Minamata disease, which first appeared in 1953 among the inhabitants of Minamata Bay in Japan and later recurred at other locations, also hit the headlines. This was caused by eating fish from the bay. Investigations led to a derelict acetylene factory, which released catalysts containing inorganic mercury compounds into a river which flowed into the bay, where they were converted by bacteria into organic mercury compounds, in particular methyl mercurials.

As with many other poisons, however, mercury compounds have sometimes been used for medicinal purposes—indeed, they were being used in China in 3000 B.C. to treat leprosy. In 1529 Paracelsus published two works dealing with venereal disease. He was influenced in this by astrological and medicinal theories, e.g. that Venus's arrows were to blame for epidemic syphilis, which should therefore be fought with the forces of Mercury. He recommended the use, in ointment form, of mercury in treating syphilis or lues: thirty-three percent mercury finely distributed in pig fat. This method of treatment is certain to have caused numerous cases of poisoning. Paracelsus was the first to produce "precipitates" (precipitations of $HgNH_2Cl$ from aqueous solutions of mercury dichloride and ammonia spirit) and basic mercury(II)-salts and to use these for medicinal purposes. Other mercury preparations, such as calomel and Hg_2Cl_2, were used in the 19th century, mainly as diuretics and disinfectants. The metal is still in use today, although not without a certain amount of controversy, in the form of mercury amalgam for filling teeth.

In the case of mercury, too, it should be noted that it is now a ubiquitous trace element; even some foodstuffs contain up to 0.1 mg/kg mercury.

Let us now turn to one of the typical light metals, namely beryllium. Beryllium and its compounds are irreplaceable these days—they are needed, for instance, in aviation and space technology, and for instruments used in neutron, X-ray and radiation technology. Strict safety measures govern their processing, because they can cause serious illness if inhaled as dust or vapour, or consumed as solutions. When work on beryllium fluoride extraction was in progress, the illness observed among the workforce was initially blamed on the fluorine, but attention then shifted to the dangers of beryllium poisoning. Since then, the lung damage caused by the element has been recognized as an industrial disease for which compensation must be paid. Little is yet known about the biochemical reasons for its toxicity. Thallium(I)-sulphate has been used since the twenties as a rat poison. Many suicides and murders can be laid at the door of this element. Even 1 g is lethal for an

adult. Thallium compounds are rapidly absorbed. They act as epithelium and nerve poisons, although their exact mechanism of action is still unknown. In the burn-ups required in the metallurgical working of ores, thallium is present as a "pollutant", and is therefore attracting more and more interest.

Toxicologists also find all compounds in which chromium is present in its hexavalent form of practical importance. Chromate and dichromate solutions are extremely corrosive: 2 to 5 g are lethal. Chromate dusts create ulcers on the mucous membranes of the respiratory tract and damage the nasal septum. These symptoms do not heal easily. Chromate is a carcinogen, and people working with this substance are particularly prone to bronchogenic cancer.

There is no room here to discuss radioactive metals. Some are important for diagnostic and therapeutic purposes, or as waste from the operation of nuclear reactors, or as "fall out" after nuclear weapons tests. The primary harmful effect of these elements is their radioactive radiation, although there are also radioactive elements which have other toxic effects apart from radiation (e.g. plutonium).

Several inorganic compounds can cause serious poisoning as salts with their anions, i.e. the non-metallic part in this case is practically irrelevant as far as toxicity is concerned. Here, too, we can consider only a few examples, although these are fairly typical.

At first sight, nitrate ions, which we encounter, for instance, in the form of calcium nitrate as Norway saltpetre, would not appear to be dangerous toxins. But nitrates can be found in many different substances, and infants can be put at great risk by foodstuffs containing nitrate. Seventy percent of these nitrates can be traced to vegetables, and twenty percent to drinking water (see p. 109).

Let us now consider another anion which contains nitrogen—cyanide. Readers of detective novels will be familiar with potassium cyanide: in chemical terms it is the potassium salt of prussic acid. Prussic acid is released in quantity by the gastric acids from potassium cyanide and sodium cyanide taken orally; both are easily soluble in water. The characteristic smell of prussic acid is like that of bitter almonds (the smell of bitter almonds also stems from traces of prussic acid, although in this case it derives from an organic bond of the cyano group). The lethal dose of potassium cyanide is about 0.15 g. Prussic acid blocks the trivalent iron of the respiratory enzyme cytochrome oxidase, which is essential for tissue respiration, so that no more oxygen can be transmitted to the tissue from the haemoglobin in the blood and carbon dioxide cannot be removed. This leads to rapid "internal suffocation". Prussic acid gas kills in a few seconds, with the victim suffering breathing difficulties and convulsions. Despite the hazards involved, gaseous prussic acid was used in pest control before better methods were found. In California, for instance, thousands of tonnes were used to control scale lice in citrus plantations.

Under its pseudonym of Zyklon B, prussic acid was used in Fascist concentration camps to kill millions of people—surely the most horrific use of poison in history.

To conclude this chapter, we should like to mention a mineral which, until the middle of the 20th century, was considered totally harmless, namely asbestos. Asbestos minerals are very widespread in the Alps and in the mountain ranges of Portugal, Turkey, Iran, Nepal and China. Asbestos is a flameproof, fibrous silicate whose natural aggregates can be deflocculated mechanically into fibres of different thicknesses and lengths. The first attempts to use Italian asbestos in technology date back to about 1860. Soon a wide range of possible uses was developed for asbestos, e.g. in flameproof fabrics, for insulation, as brake linings, etc. In 1977, world production amounted to 5,779,000 tons. Today there is no disputing the carcinogenic effects of asbestos dust. The latent period for asbestos-related cancer is fifteen to thirty-five years. Meanwhile, substitutes for asbestos have been introduced or are undergoing tests all over the world.

From the point of view of medicinal toxicology, asbestos cannot be classified directly alongside poisons in the classical sense, but the opinion is increasingly gaining ground that all long-term effects and delayed harmful effects (including cancers and most hereditary defects) connected with elements and their inorganic—and also organic—compounds are, in the final analysis, the results of poisoning caused by environmental factors.

Thallium(I)-sulphate has been used as a rat poison since the 1920s. Thallium often appears as a concomitant of pyrite. One of the few thallium minerals is crocosite, which is very rare.

The age of industrialization brought not only progress, but also environmental
pollution, as a view of 19th-century Sheffield shows.
City Library, Sheffield.

Michael Faraday in his London laboratory. In 1825, he became the first person to produce the pesticide hexachlorocyclohexane, which is still used today. Royal Institution, London.

The chemical industry nowadays makes great endeavours to prevent environmental pollution: BASF's biological effluent purification plant at Ludwigshafen (Federal Republic of Germany) has the capacity to treat the sewage of a city of six to seven million people.

Modern chemical plants can now be regarded as safe: phosgene plant BASF in Ludwigshafen (Federal Republic of Germany).

Various types of protective clothing used in the chemical industry.

Following page:
Research work, too, demands strict safety precautions.

Deadly technology?

(Synthetic poisons in our environment)

If we now turn briefly to synthetic poisons, then we are considering a field of toxicology that is only about one hundred years old, as old as technical chemistry, or the industrial large-scale production of chemical products. Of course, even in pre-industrial times various chemical products such as medicines, dyes, tanning agents, soaps, lubricants, glues and so on were being manufactured, but the production of chemicals by the ton only became possible with modern technology and energy supplies.

Every age has its own characteristics and peculiarities, and experience is gained according to the old saw that man learns by his mistakes. This is also true for the production and use of poisons which have, to an ever increasing extent, penetrated nearly all spheres of human activity in the last hundred years, and even into our private lives. The first impulse of many people is to protest that they have, and wish to have, nothing to do with industrial toxins. But everyone knows what modern chemistry can achieve and that we are indebted to it for many household products, as well as newspapers, carpets, even battery-operated transistor radios, not to mention all of the aids with which we cultivate flowers, kill weeds and harvest worm-free fruit. This list of everyday applications of chemistry could be extended by hundreds more products: household articles and pet products are just as important on this list as requisites for amateur sports and hobbies. But these products are all chemical substances which are, in some way or another, active—substances which we indeed wish to be active, if we are using them to protect plants in the garden or for baking and frying, seasoning and preserving in the kitchen, or to enhance our leisure time—a drink from the bottle, a draw at the cigarette, television pictures, tranquillizers, the contraceptive pill and even the whiff of Chanel Nr. 5—all owe a great deal to chemistry.

Chemistry is a knowledge of materials, in the widest sense. This includes knowledge about how materials behave in the molecular environment of our biosphere.

In former decades, chemistry was expected to concentrate chiefly on the application of laboratory findings to the world of industrial production, i.e. iron and steel. Although this is still the case, legislators—that is, in the final analysis, society—are imposing ever stricter and more urgent conditions on the chemical industry in which environmental protection plays a much more important role than in the past.

The chemical industry is also faced with similar demands from a wide range of industries to supply new products which are required for the purposes of environmental protection. This ranges from non-degradable plastic materials to new propellants for aerosols, and aids and detoxicants for the disposal of pollutants. The re-cycling of waste products should be regarded as an important part of the chemical industry's contribution to environmental protection.

Throughout the world, it is estimated that some fifty thousand substances in about a million preparations with a weight of several million tons are now produced, sold and used every year. These substances and preparations, as well as their decomposition and waste products, are known as environmental chemicals. These are defined as those substances which enter the environment as a result of human activity, or come into being in the environment as by-products, whether this is intentional or not.

The overwhelming majority of environmental chemicals are alien to nearly all ecosystems, apart from the few cases where waste products are identical to compounds formed by natural materials. Such alien substances can harm man, animals or plants, depending on their chemical structure, their quantity or concentration and the nature and duration of exposure to them.

The harmful effect of a substance can be acute, or can take the form of chronic poisoning, which manifests itself in harmful long-term effects.

Mediaeval "plant protection": the bishop of Lausanne anathematizes the cockchafer during a plague in 1497. Contemporary illustration.

We know little about the nature and actual degree of the harmful effects occasioned by the overwhelming majority of environmental chemicals which are of practical relevance today. Initially, therefore, the degree of risk involved is usually only a matter of guesswork. The real crux of the matter, as far as the interplay between chemistry and the environment is concerned, has been, is and remains the extent to which man is prepared to take risks. For many decades, the chemical industry has been able to claim that it is one of the industries which recognized the needs of environmental protection relatively early with regard to the influence of their products on the environment. Other sectors of the economy gave much less priority to this issue: to name just two examples, agriculture and transport contribute more than ever to large-scale environmental pollution. Such negative effects are then blamed wholesale on the chemical industry by people who should know better, but it can hardly be held responsible if agricultural chemicals are not used according to instructions, or if engines are not properly maintained; nor can it be held responsible for oil tanker disasters. It is relevant to remind readers that, in the European industrialized States, the chemical industry is only the fifth worst offender in terms of industrial diseases. We must also note that, of all cases of industrial diseases in the European chemical industry during the last decade, an average of twelve to fifteen percent took the form of poisoning, the same portion of occupational skin diseases and forty-six to forty-eight percent of hearing defects caused by noise.

The situation looks different if one considers the statistics on fatalities, however, because hardness of hearing is not fatal. In the case of poisoning, despite improved medical first-aid and therapeutical methods, two to three percent of industrial accidents are fatal.

If one analyzes the international statistics for poisoning, one gets an even clearer picture of the overall situation regarding the toxicological effects of environmental pollution. Medicines are by far the most common cause of severe acute poisoning in the industrial world, being responsible in sixty to sixty-five percent of cases—although one must remember that only five to six percent of emergency cases admitted to hospital result from poisoning. Chemical and technical products, including household and agricultural chemicals, are responsible for only thirteen to fourteen percent of severe cases of acute poisoning. If one considers long-term effects, however, the picture is quite different, because according to the WHO, seventy to eighty percent of cancer cases, for instance, are caused by environmental factors. All the statistics published by the WHO and other bodies show that cigarette-smoking, drinking high-percentage alcohol to excess, drug abuse and a poor diet are the main risk factors for cancer and heart and circulatory disorders. These causes are followed by atmospheric pollution resulting from traffic, fossil fuels and out-dated power stations. Only then do we come to accidental poisoning by the acute and chronic effects of chemical and technical products.

Of course, every industrial nation today has more or less unambiguous legislation governing the handling of poisons, from production to consumption, and the disposal of the remainder or of that which is no longer required. The new poison laws of the German Democratic Republic and the legislation on chemicals in the Federal Republic of Germany are examples of initiatives which are designed to suit the modern needs of industrial societies with a substantial chemical industry. There is as yet, however, no comprehensive international legislation. Nevertheless, no-one should be under any illusion that more laws mean more safety. Just as forecasts are no substitute for experience, so laws can create no real order in an area where only the greatest care in what are apparently the most minor questions of safety, regular instruction on existing rules and regulations and regular training on how to cope with emergencies are the best guarantee of minimizing risks and coping effectively with the dangers which are inevitably present for man and his environment. When pollution scandals hit the headlines yet again, however, this only goes to show how irresponsibly some of our fellow-citizens act against the common good.

When one is considering the subject of poison in the environment, one must take into account that the problems of understanding reactions are made all the more complex by the fact that metabolic processes occur in the human organism which are influenced in turn in ways we do not fully understand by alien substances and pollutants. At the same time, moreover, biological and toxic effects can be influenced by medicines, alcohol, tobacco products and even beauty products, cleaning agents and cosmetics.

Of course, things today are no longer quite as they were in the time of Voltaire who, with reference to medical knowledge at that time, said sarcastically that "Doctors pour medicaments, of which they know little, in order to cure diseases of which they know even less, into people, of whom they know nothing at all". Even so, as far as the introduction of chemicals into our "personal environment" is concerned, Voltaire's remark still rings true today.

So great are the already apparent effects of synthetic poisons that such poisoning of our environment can no longer be allowed to continue at the rate with which it is currently progressing, if we are prepared to accept responsibility for future generations. It is man who is wholly responsible for the safe, low-risk use of chemical products and thus also for synthetic poisons. It is quite clear that we are dealing today with the omnipresent existence of thousands of industrial chemicals, which are alien substances in the environment of each and every one of us. But it is not a case of accepting or rejecting chemical products: rather, we should be asking "where?", "what?", "how much?" and "how dangerous?".

Probably the first synthetic poison about which such questions were asked by a few far-sighted toxicologists—as well as by the novelist Rachel Carson in her highly controversial book *Silent Spring*—was dichloro-diphenyl-trichloro-ethane—known in the literature as DDT for short. This is now regarded throughout the world as the archetypal synthetic

$$Cl - C_6H_4 - \underset{\underset{CCl_3}{|}}{CH} - C_6H_4 - Cl$$

poison, with many repercussions on the environment. DDT can today be found in the body fat of nearly all human beings all over the world as well as in the body fat of penguins at the South Pole and snow geese in the far North. Although its ubiquitous presence does not mean it is a dangerous poison, it does not exactly prove that it is harmless either. Paul Hermann Müller, the man who discovered this substance, which was, and still is, an excellent means of controlling some previously uncontrollable pests and pathogens, won the Nobel Prize (quite deservedly!) in 1948. Today the main value of DDT is seen in the way it has sparked off global discussions on the environment. We have known for a long time that there are other such halogenated hydrocarbons, which are used all over the world and some of which are much more poisonous than DDT, and much more dangerous for future generations. A glaring example is dioxin, which won sad notoriety through the Vietnam War and the Seveso catastrophe, chemically known as 2,3,7,8-tetrachloro-dibenzo-p-dioxin, or TCDD for short. We do not yet know very

much about why this molecule is so extremely toxic for man and some animals. If only two chlorine atoms are changed in this molecule, then the resulting isomeric 1,2,3,4-tetrachloro-dibenzo-p-dioxin can be regarded as practically harmless. Every analytical chemist now knows that there are hundreds of organochlorine compounds of industrial origin in this world we live in. In all probability, some of these affect our well-being and health, although it is not possible for us to find out more about this at present. For example, what conclusions can an environmentalist draw from the fact that at every point in the northern hemisphere of this planet—whether near or far from human habitation—the concentration of tetrachlorethylene has been 10^{12} molecules per litre of air since about the 1930s? He and the legislators responsible can at least establish from this fact that the capacity of the atmosphere to decontaminate itself is no longer sufficient in the presence of such alien matter. And this is not only true for the air, which we inhale along with these pollutants of varying toxicity both day and night. It is true in a sometimes even more dramatic way for the water which we drink, in which we bathe and which we use to prepare our food! The water resources of the Earth are still regarded far too often as inexhaustible, and the oceans are abused as refuse disposal dumps. And yet in the North Sea, for instance, only fifty-four tons of a poison (two to three goods-waggon loads) is sufficient to create a concentration of pollutants of 1 µg/l water. If the chemical is not biodegradable, then this concentration can be dangerously high. One should also consider oil tanker accidents, when thousands of tons of crude oil poison the sea, against this background, not to mention the natural excrement of humans and their livestock. All too often, the situation is seen only in territorial terms, and it is forgotten that air and ocean currents can spread toxic pollutants over thousands of kilometres in a matter of weeks, months or years. Chemical conversions take place, sometimes in the form of decontamination, but sometimes also as poisoning. These poisoning processes are not always as measureable or even as visible to everyone as the way acid rain is killing trees throughout wide areas of Europe, or the ecological collapse in parts of the sea where the water reaches a degree of acidity that approaches that of the dilute mineral acids which are used only in laboratories. The phenol level of some rivers is so high that the water can be used to develop films, not to mention some toxic metals such as mercury and cadmium which are fed by the rivers into the seas by the ton every day, and which far outstrip the quantities produced by mines in earlier centuries. The present situation as far as environmental pollution is concerned is the result of technical developments which have come to pass in only a hundred years.

Synthetic poisons in the environment are pollutants which are produced not by nature but by man, whether deliberately or unintentionally, often thoughtlessly and without misgivings, and which threaten him and everything around him. Only man is capable of breaking out of this vicious circle, into which his own short-sightedness has driven him. This can be done without jeopardizing industrial and social progress, and without the spread of cultural pessimism and civilizational fear. All that is needed is reason, and—as Bertolt Brecht said—the victory of reason must be the victory of the reasonable.

This brief chapter on synthetic poisons, and with it this book about the wide range of poisonous substances, cannot be concluded without a few pertinent remarks on the misuse of poisons for military purposes. On 22nd April 1915, the poisonous gas chlorine became the first modern weapon of mass extermination when it was used by imperial German troops at Ypres in Flanders on the advice of Fritz Haber, who later won the Nobel Prize. Since then, there has been an unprecedented escalation in the development of chemical weapons as military and sabotage poisons. We do not intend to go into historical details here, nor to examine the military toxins which exist today. But to conclude a book of this nature, it must be made perfectly clear that a war in which the sophisticated poisons available today were used, whether we are talking about V-agents, which kill instantly and are based on organophosphorous binary systems, or "only" the extremely effective, non-lethal neurotoxins which create mass terror, would be a crime against humanity.

Appendix

Subject index

quercitrin 78
quinine 105
quinolizidine alkaloids 80
quinones 108

Radianthus sp. 124
Ranunculaceae 80, 81, 108
rape 83
Rauwolfia serpentina 106
red beech 82
red firefish 124
red-staining inocybe 71
red stinging jellyfish 118
repelling substances 118
reserpine 106
rhododendron 120
Rhododendron ponticum 120
rhubarb 82
Rhus toxicodendron 79
ricin 85, 86
ricinine 86
ricinoleic acid *see* 12-hydroxy-oleic acid
Ricinus communis 85
Rivea corymbosa 27
robin 80
Robinia pseudoacacia 80
rosary pea 86
rotenones 87, 88
Rubiaceae 35, 105, 106
russula 69
Russula sp. 69

sabinene 84
sabinol 84
Saccharum officinarum 81
safrole 111
Salamandra salamandra 122
Salamandra sp. 115
salmonellae 75
salvarsan 10, 145
sand viper 140
sanguinarine 111
saponins 78, 80, 82, 106, 108
sassafras oil 111
saw-scaled viper 141
saxitoxin 77, 117, 123
scopolamine 13, 85
Scorpaenidae 119
scorpion fish 124
scorpions 119, 120, 126, 136

Scorzonera hispanica 82
Scrophulariaceae 106
sea anemones 119, 124
sea cucumber 115, 119
sea slugs 118
sea snakes 132, 140
sea wasp 118
seed protectants 149
selenoamino acids 108
serotonin 29, 120
shiitake 71
shrubby horsetail (sea-grape) 68
Sieva bean 81
silphium 18
Silybum marianum 106
silymarin 106
Sinapis alba 108
sinigrin 83
snake venom 114, 130, 138, 139, 140, 141
Solanaceae 13, 16, 25, 42, 60, 85
solanidine 84
solanine 84
Solanum nigrum 42
Solanum tuberosum 84
Solenopsis sp. 120
South American rattlesnake 139, 141
Spanish fly 26, 85, 105, 113
Spanish mussels 117
spiders 126, 138
spindle tree 78, 80
spotted salamander 122
spurge laurel 110
staphylococci 75
star fish 119
steroid alkaloids 82, 84, 116
steroid glycosides 84, 106, 119
steroids 114, 116
stimulants 9, 10, 12, 13, 16, 27, 29, 37, 52, 67, 68
stingray 112, 119
strophantins 87
Strophantus gratus 87
Strophantus kombé 87
strychnine 86, 99
Strychnos nux-vomica 86, 99
Strychnos toxifera 86
sugar cane 81
sweet potato (batata) 81

Tanghinia venenifera 105

tanghinin 105
tannic acid 40, 65
tannin 80, 82, 106
tarantula 112, 113, 138, 139
Taricha sp. 115
Taricha torosa 115
Taxaceae 80
taxicatigenin 108
taxine 80
Taxus baccata 78, 80, 108
TCDD *see* 2,3,7,8-tetrachloro-dibenzo-p-dioxin
tea 12, 37, 38, 39, 40, 47, 50, 57, 66
tench 117
Teonanácatl 28, 43
Tephrosia vogeli 87
tetrachlorethylene 164
1,2,3,4-tetrachloro-dibenzo-p-dioxin 164
2,3,7,8-tetrachloro-dibenzo-p-dioxin 164
Δ^9-tetrahydrocannabinol 30
Tetraodontidae 116, 124
tetrodotoxin 115, 116, 124
thallium(I)-compounds 149, 151, 153
thebaine 35
theine 37
theobromine 38, 57
theophylline 38, 40
theriac 33, 46, 47
thornapple 13, 14, 16, 25, 26, 85
α-thujaplicin 101, 108
Thuja sp. 101
thujol 84
thyme 108
thymol 108
Thymus serpyllum 108
thyrosin 83
thyroxine 83
tigliane 109
Tinca tinca 117
toad poison 28, 70, 108, 114
tobacco 39, 54, 55, 60, 61, 62, 63, 65, 66
tomatine 84
tomato 84
touchwood 71
toxalbumine *see* lectins
C-toxiferine I 87
Trachinidae 119
Trachinus draco 119, 124
tree-climbing frogs 115
Tricholoma auratum 69

Index of persons

Bibliography

Toxicological works based on the history of culture

ALTHEIM, K.-H.: *Medikamente—Gifte—Drogen*. Mannheim, 1972.
BASSUS, W.: *Gifte im Tierreich*. Wittenberg, 1965.
BÖSE, G.: *Im Blauen Dunst*. Stuttgart, 1957.
BRAU, J.-L.: *L'Histoire de la drogue*. Paris, 1968.
ENGEL, F.-M.: *Die Giftküche der Natur*. Hanover, 1972.
ENGEL, F.-M.: *Zauberpflanzen—Pflanzenzauber*. Hanover, 1978.
GARDNER, G. B.: *Witchcraft today*. London, no date.
GILG, E., and P. N. SCHÜRHOFF: *Aus dem Reiche der Drogen. Geschichtliche, kulturgeschichtliche und botanische Betrachtungen über wichtige Drogen*. Dresden, 1926.
GOLOWIN, S.: *Die Magie der verbotenen Märchen. Von Hexenkräutern und Feendrogen*. Hamburg, 1974.
HABERMEHL, G.: *Gifttiere und ihre Waffen*. Berlin, Heidelberg, New York, 1983.
HABERMEHL, G.: *Venomous Animals and their Toxins*. Berlin, Heidelberg, New York, 1981.
HOFMANN, A.: *LSD—Mein Sorgenkind*. Stuttgart, 1979.
KAISER, E., and H. MICHL: *Die Biochemie der tierischen Gifte*. Vienna, 1958.
KLOBUSNITZKY, D. de: *Giftschlangen und Schlangengifte*. Munich, 1960.
KLOOS, W.: *Tabak-Kollegium*. Bremen, 1967.
LANGE, O.: *Mineral- und Pflanzengifte*. Stuttgart, 1929.
LEWIN, L.: *Die Fruchtabtreibung durch Gifte und andere Mittel*. Berlin, 1925.
LEWIN, L.: *Die Gifte in der Weltgeschichte*. Heidelberg, 1920 and Hildesheim, 1971.
LEWIN, L.: "Gifte und Gegengifte", in: *Chemiker-Zeitung*, No. 134, 1909.
LEWIN, L.: *Gifte und Vergiftungen*. Berlin, 1929.
LEWIN, L.: *Gottesurteile durch Gifte und andere Verfahren*. Berlin, 1929.
LEWIN, L.: *Die Pfeilgifte*. Leipzig, 1923.
LEWIN, L.: *Phantastica. Die betäubenden und erregenden Genussmittel*. Berlin, 1924.
LINDNER, E.: *Toxikologie der Nahrungsmittel*. Stuttgart, New York, 1979.
MAURIZO, A.: *Geschichte der gegorenen Getränke*. Munich, 1933 and Wiesbaden, 1970.
PORTIGLIOTTI, G.: *Die Familie Borgia*. Stuttgart, 1923.
RÖMPP, H., and J. SCHURZ: *Chemische Zaubertränke. Anregung und Genuss—Rausch und Sucht*. Stuttgart, 1972.
SCHENK, G.: *Das Buch der Gifte*. Berlin (West), 1954.
SCHULTES, R., and A. HOFMANN: *Pflanzen der Götter*. Bern, Stuttgart, 1980.
SCHURZ, J.: *Vom Bilsenkraut zum LSD*. Stuttgart, 1970.
SÖHN, G.: *Von Mokka bis Espresso*. Hamburg, 1957.
ULISCHBERGER, E.: *Rund um den Branntwein*. Leipzig, 1983.
ULISCHBERGER, E.: *Rund ums Bier*. Leipzig, 1977.

Toxicological handbooks and textbooks

Animal Toxins. Edited by F. E. RUSSEL and P. R. SAUNDERS. Oxford, 1967.
ARENA, J. M.: *Poisoning. Chemistry, Symptoms, Treatments*. Springfield, 1973.
CASARETT, L. J., and J. DOULL: *Toxicology*. New York, 1975.
DREISBACH, R. H.: *Handbook of Poisoning: Diagnosis and Treatment*. Los Altos, 1974.
FABREM, R., and R. TRUHAUT: *Précis de toxicologie*, 2 vols. No place, 1965.
FATTORUSSO, V., and O. RITTER: *Dictionnaire de pharmacologie clinique à l'usage du médecin, du pharmacien et de l'étudiant*. Paris, 1967.
FORTH, W., HENSCHLER, D., and W. RUMMEL: *Allgemeine und spezielle Pharmakologie und Toxikologie*. Mannheim, Vienna, Zurich, 1977.
FOURNIER, E., and P. GERVAIS: *Dictionnaire des intoxications*. Paris, 1970.
FRÉJAVILLE, J. P.: *Toxicologie clinique et analytique*. Paris, 1975.
FROHNE, D., and J. PFÄNDER: *Giftpflanzen*. Stuttgart, 1983.
GESSNER, O.: *Gift- und Arzneipflanzen in Mitteleuropa*. Heidelberg, 1974.
GRAEBNER, K. E.: *Natur—Reich der tausend Wunder*. Gütersloh, 1971.
GRAHAM, J. D. P.: *The Diagnosis of Acute Poisoning*. Baltimore, 1969.
KOENEN, E.: *Heil- und Giftpflanzen in Süd-West-Afrika*. Windhoek, 1977.
KROEBER, L.: *Das neuzeitliche Kräuterbuch*, Vol. 3: *Giftpflanzen*. Stuttgart, 1938.
Lehrbuch der Pharmakologie und Toxikologie. Edited by H. BADER. Weinheim, Deerfield Beach (Florida), Basle, 1982.
LEUENBERGER, H.: *Gesund durch Gift*. Stuttgart, 1972.
LIEBENOW, H., and K. LIEBENOW: *Giftpflanzen*. Jena, 1981.
LOHS, K.: *Synthetische Gifte*. Berlin, 1974.
LUDEWIG, R., and K. LOHS: *Akute Vergiftungen*. Jena, 1981.
MARTINETZ, D.: *Arsenik · Curare · Coffein—Gifte in unserer Welt*. Leipzig, 1982.
MATTHEW, H., and A. A. H. LAWSON: *Treatment of Common Acute Poisoning*. Edinburgh, 1975.
MOESCHLIN, S.: *Klinik und Therapie der Vergiftungen*. Stuttgart, New York, 1980.
MOESCHLIN, S.: *Poisoning: Diagnosis and Treatment*. New York, 1965.
MOREAU, C.: *Moulds, Toxins and Food*. Chichester, 1979
NORTH, P. M.: *Poisonous Plants and Fungi*. London, 1967.
PAHLOW, M.: *Das grosse Buch der Heilpflanzen*. Munich, 1979.
RADELEFT, R. D.: *Veterinary Toxicology*. Philadelphia, 1970.
RÜCHT, U.: *Heil- und Giftpflanzen*. Stuttgart, 1977.
THIENES, C. H., and T. J. Halley: *Clinical Toxicology*, Philadelphia, 1972.
WIRTH, W., and C. GLOXHUBER: *Toxikologie*. Stuttgart, New York, 1981.

Sources of illustrations

ADN/Zentralbild, Berlin pp. 47 bottom left, 48 bottom left, 48 bottom right, 50 top, 50 bottom, 62 left
BASF, Ludwigshafen pp. 156, 157, 158, 159, 160
Bergmann, Klaus, Potsdam pp. 55 bottom, 56 top
Bibliothèque Nationale, Paris p. 18 top and bottom
City Library, Sheffield p. 154
Deutsche Fotothek, Dresden pp. 20, 41, 45 top and bottom, 54 bottom, 110
Deutsche Staatsbibliothek, Berlin p. 89 left
Fiedler, Werner, Leipzig pp. 123, 125 bottom right
Förster, Manfred, Leipzig pp. 46 top, 104
Görner, Herbert, Leipzig p. 90 top left and bottom right
Grambow, Axel, Berlin p. 128
Hänse, Ingrid, Leipzig pp. 30, 32 right, 34, 48 top, 57, 66, 137, 139, 144
Hecker, E., Heidelberg p. 103
Herschel, Kurt, Holzhausen pp. 44 left, 92 left
Hosking, Eric & David, London p. 130 bottom
Kage, Manfred, Lauterstein p. 92 right
Karger-Decker, Bernt, Berlin pp. 15, 33 right, 63, 73, 74, 77, 91, 107, 146, 147, 168
Karpinski, Jürgen, Dresden, pp. 135, 136, 153
Kühlmann, Dietrich, Berlin pp. 125 top left, 125 top right, 125 bottom left
Köhler, Berlin p. 99 left
Kulturamt Stadt Hanau p. 46 bottom
Kunsthistorisches Museum, Vienna pp. 19 (Photo Meyer), 93
Linden-Museum/Ursula Didoni, Stuttgart p. 143 top left
Martin-von-Wagner-Museum/University of Würzburg p. 59
MAS, Barcelona p. 21
Metropolitan Museum of Art, New York p. 95
Müller, R. Klaus, Leipzig p. 89
Museum für Völkerkunde, Staatliche Museen Preussischer Kulturbesitz, Berlin (West) p. 43 top right
Národní Galeri, Prague/Jaroslav Jeřábek p. 129
Needon, Christoph, Leipzig p. 96 right
Österreichische Nationalbibliothek, Vienna p. 23
Pelizaeus-Museum, Hildesheim p. 52 top
Petri, Joachim, Mölkau pp. 36, 42 left, 47 bottom right, 51, 62 right, 83, 113
Plessing, Carin, Leipzig pp. 42 right, 43 bottom, 90 top right, 90 bottom left, 94, 96 left, 100, 124

Publishers' archives pp. 25, 32, 38, 39, 58, 79, 134
Publishing house E. A. Seemann, Leipzig p. 54 top
Rauh, W., Heidelberg p. 44 right
Reinhold, Gerhard, Mölkau pp. 53, 56
Royal Institution, London p. 155
Rudloff, Klaus, Berlin pp. 121 top and bottom, 122 top, 126, 127 top and bottom, 130 top, 131, 132
Sandig, Christoph, Leipzig p. 24
Sembritzki, Christa, Leipzig pp. 14, 16, 27, 29, 32, 33 left, 40, 52 bottom, 65, 67, 70, 82, 84, 85, 88, 105, 142, 150
Schmidt-Glassner, Helga, Stuttgart pp. 22, 47 top, 102
Staatliche Graphische Sammlung, Munich p. 72
Staatliche Museen, Berlin frontispiece, p. 101
Thüringisches Museum, Eisenach p. 17
Trutnau, Ludwig, Altrich p. 133 top and bottom
Vogel, Andreas, Leipzig p. 99 right
Wieckhorst, Karin, Leipzig p. 49
Wiesner, Horst, Berlin p. 122 bottom
Wustmann, Erich, Bad Schandau pp. 97, 98

The further illustrations were taken from the following publications:

Hartwich, C.: *Die menschlichen Genussmittel. Ihre Herkunft, Verbreitung, Geschichte, Anwendung, Bestandteile und Wirkung.* Leipzig, 1911 pp. 34, 48 top, 66
Hochstetter, M. C. F.: *Die Giftgewächse Deutschlands und der Schweiz.* Stuttgart/Esslingen, no date pp. 29, 40, 42 right, 94, 96 left, 100
Koehlers Medicinal-Pflanzen in naturgetreuen Abbildungen. Berlin, 1923 pp. 32 left, 65, 67, 88, 105
Lonitzer, Adam: *Kreütterbuch.* Frankfurt, 1582 p. 14
Meyers Grosses Konversations-Lexikon. Leipzig/Vienna, 1909, Vol. 18 p. 139
Rausch und Realität. Drogen im Kulturvergleich. Materialienband zu einer Ausstellung im Rautenstrauch-Jost-Museum für Völkerkunde der Stadt Köln. Cologne, 1981 p. 57
Sammlung Naturkundlicher Tafeln. Edited by Erich Cramer. Hamburg, 1961 p. 90 top right and bottom left
Voelkner, K.: *Von Werwölfen und anderen Tiermenschen.* Leipzig, 1924 p. 16
Winkler, Eduard: *Sämtliche Giftgewächse Deutschlands.* Leipzig, 1854 pp. 82, 84